The Politics of Nuclear Power

# The Politics of Nuclear Power

## Dave Elliott

with Pat Coyne, Mike George and Roy Lewis

Pluto  Press

First published 1978 by Pluto Press Limited
Unit 10 Spencer Court
7 Chalcot Road, London NW1 8LH

Copyright © Pluto Press 1978
ISBN 0 86104 028 7

Designed by Colin Bailey
Cover designed by Terry Seago

Photoset by Bristol Typesetting Company Limited
Barton Manor, St Philips, Bristol
Printed in Great Britain by Cox & Wyman Ltd
London, Fakenham and Reading

# Contents

## List of Abbreviations

| | |
|---|---|
| AGR | Advanced Gas-Cooled Reactor |
| BNFL | British Nuclear Fuels Ltd |
| BWR | Boiling Water Reactor |
| CEGB | Central Electricity Generating Board |
| CHP | Combined Heat and Power systems |
| FBR | Fast Breeder Reactor |
| mtce | millions of tons of coal equivalent |
| PWR | Pressurised Water Reactor |
| SGHWR | Steam Generating Heavy Water Reactor |
| UKAEA | United Kingdom Atomic Energy Authority |

## Energy units

| | |
|---|---|
| KW | kilo watt |
| KWh | kilo watt hours |
| MW | mega watt = 1,000 kilo watts |
| GW | giga watt = 1,000 mega watts |
| TW | tera watt = 1,000 giga watts |
| TWh | tera watt hours |

A typical one-bar electric fire consumes about 1KW per hour

# Introduction *Dave Elliott*

This book focuses on a number of problems, questions and issues relating to nuclear power likely to be of concern to workers in the nuclear industry and elsewhere. It is divided into three main parts:

## Part 1. The political economy of nuclear power
Who benefits? Who pays? Is nuclear power economically viable? What are the long-term aims of the giant multi-national corporations that dominate the industry? What is the role of government and what are the institutional pressures forcing nuclear power on us? What is the attitude of the trade-union leadership?

## Part 2. Nuclear power and employment
What are the health and safety implications for workers in the nuclear industry? Will nuclear power lead to infringements of trade-union rights? Will it create jobs? What about alternative energy options? Is a non-nuclear strategy viable in terms of energy and jobs?

## Part 3. Political strategies
What are the aims of the anti-nuclear movement? How do they relate to the concerns of trade unionists? What demands should trade unionists make in regard to nuclear power?

It is not our aim to provide an exhaustive treatment of all the technical, economic, social and environmental problems of nuclear power. Many of these have been dealt with adequately elsewhere and some suggestions for further reading are given on page 140. However it may be useful to begin with a simple guide to some of the basic technology involved and a brief survey of the development of nuclear power in the UK and overseas.

## What is Nuclear Power?

The atoms of a certain type of uranium, uranium 235, can be made to undergo 'fission' or split apart, producing heat energy and radiation. The heat can be used like heat from burning coal or oil, to raise steam and turn turbogenerators and thus produce electricity. Nuclear fission reactions need careful control because, under certain conditions, an uncontrolled chain reaction can lead to an atomic explosion, as a result of the instantaneous emission of vast quantities of heat. All reactors are designed so that this cannot happen. However, the radiation emitted in normal operations and the radioactive products of the fission are highly dangerous to living things—the effects of exposure range from death within hours, to the development of cancers many years later and the production of genetic modifications in offspring, depending on the type and intensity of the radiation. Extensive precautions must be, and are, made to avoid exposure to radiation and contamination by radioactive material.

Fissionable (or 'fissile') uranium 235 occurs in only very small amounts in natural uranium—the bulk of it is uranium 238, which itself cannot undergo fission. To make reactor fuel, natural uranium is usually 'enriched' so that the amount of 235 available for fission is increased. To make 'weapons grade' material suitable for an atomic bomb, enrichment must be carried even further—up to 90 per cent U235 or more.

In a nuclear reactor the fission process produces 'fast' (high energy) neutron particles, which after they have slowed by colliding with other atoms (a process called thermalisation) sustain the nuclear chain reaction, by causing subsequent fissions of other U235 atoms. This is the basis of the *thermal reactor*. But the neutrons also have an effect on the U238 component of the fuel—it is converted into a new material, *plutonium*, which is itself fissionable.

This is the material used in most atomic bombs. But it can also be used to fuel reactors.

## Nuclear Power in the UK

At present nuclear power plants supply less than 4 per cent of Britain's primary energy, or about 12 per cent of its electricity.

Most of this power comes from the first-generation *Magnox reactors*, fuelled with uranium clad in Magnox alloy cans and cooled by carbon dioxide gas. The first of these was built in the 1950s at Calder Hall near Windscale, and eleven others were subsequently built. They have proved relatively trouble-free, unlike the second-generation *Advanced Gas-Cooled Reactors* (AGRs) which have been beset with technical problems and delays for years. Over-run costs of

Dungeness B have been put at £104 million and of Hinkley Point B £33 million, and the Hunterston B plant had to be shut down in late 1977 following the accidental ingress of sea water, with estimated repair costs of £20 million. In addition to the existing five AGRs, a further two have now been given the go-ahead. An earlier contender, the *Steam Generating Heavy Water Reactor* (SGHWR) has been abandoned.

All these 'thermal' reactors will inevitably produce some plutonium as a by-product. However, another type of reactor—the *Fast Breeder Reactor* (FBR)—has been developed, which produces or 'breeds' plutonium more efficiently (as mentioned earlier it is possible to convert uranium 238, which is otherwise unusable, into fissionable plutonium, which can then be used either to re-fuel the breeder reactor or in conventional reactors). The first British breeder was built at Dounreay in the 1950s; a second prototype there came on power in 1975. The nuclear industry would like to push ahead with a programme of breeder reactor development, starting with a large-scale commercial fast reactor, since there are clearly limits to the reserves of uranium 235 fuel used in coventional thermal reactors.

All reactors produce *active nuclear wastes* (fission products) as well as plutonium, and the spent fuel is periodically removed from the reactor and 'reprocessed' to separate valuable plutonium from the wastes. In Britain this is done at the Windscale reprocessing works. High-activity wastes have to be stored for many centuries before they are safe.

At present, these wastes are kept in liquid form in double-walled tanks under strictly controlled conditions. There are hopes that the wastes can eventually be vitrified (glassified) and stored underground, although so far the process for doing this has not been proved on a commercial scale. The development of a breeder reactor programme would increase the amount of material that had to be reprocessed and would probably increase the amount of plutonium in transit round the country. At present nuclear materials are moved by land and sea (and in some cases air) in carefully constructed and guarded containers. About half of the uranium ore for the British nuclear programme comes from South Africa, most of the remainder from Canada. There are also reserves in Namibia and Australia. The USA and the USSR both have considerable reserves of their own.

Britain was the first country to operate a commercial nuclear plant and has considerable expertise in the field. The British gas-cooled reactors are widely considered safer than the American water-cooled plants, the *Pressurised Water Reactor* (PWR) and the *Boiling Water Reactor* (BWR), although only two Magnox reactors have been sold abroad. 80 per cent of the reactors in the world are of US design. However, Britain is currently offering fuel reprocessing facilities to Japan and, as chapter 2 illustrates, providing technical aid to a number of other countries.

In Britain, long-term plans for expansion beyond the current dozen or so operating plants have been under review for some time (see chapter 1). The UKAEA's programme as submitted to the Flowers Royal Commission on Environmental Pollution in 1976 was based on the prediction that we shall need 365GW of nuclear energy by the year 2025—about fifty times our present nuclear capacity— which implies the construction of the equivalent of around 280 1.25GW AGRs over the next fifty years. By the year 2000 we shall need, say, 105GW—that's 84 AGRs representing a seven-fold expansion. In fact not all of these would be AGRs and as Table 1 below illustrates, the UKAEA would like to push ahead with a major fast breeder programme. The subsequent Green Paper on energy policy (Cmnd. 7101, HMSO 1978) scaled down this

**Table 1**
UKAEA projected programme, installed capacity in GW at end of the year

| Year | Thermal | Fast | Total Nuclear |
|------|---------|------|---------------|
| 1980 | 11 | — | 11 |
| 1985 | 14 | 1 | 15 |
| 1990 | 26 | 4 | 30 |
| 1995 | 45 | 19 | 64 |
| 2000 | 71 | 33 | 104 |
| 2010 | 104 | 89 | 193 |
| 2020 | 104 | 200 | 304 |
| 2030 | 56 | 370 | 426 |

Source: Royal Commission on Environmental Pollution; Sixth Report, *Nuclear Power and the Environment* (Cmnd. 6618, HMSO 1976. The 'Flowers' Report, after its chairman, Sir Brian Flowers, Rector of Imperial College and member of the Board of UKAEA.)

Note: The Flowers Report comments: 'The AEA programme (104GW in 2000) . . . was considerably smaller than that originally advanced in their evidence (149GW in 2000) and much smaller than that calculated as desirable in a companion document (210–285GW) in 2000)'.

programme dramatically—to 40 GW by the year 2000, this figure including existing plants. But even that implies about 24 new stations before the end of the century, at a cost of perhaps £24 billion.

## Nuclear Power Worldwide

The British nuclear programme is dwarfed by the US programme: at one stage there were plans for 2,000 units by the year 2000. The US already has 67 operating reactors and another 156 under construction or on the drawing board. In the longer term a further 200 or so are planned, so that the total by the year 2000 could be about 400.

Accurate up-to-date figures are difficult to locate, but Japan and France are both known to be looking for an eight-fold expansion. Japan already has thirteen plants operating and a further eleven under construction, and has considered a programme for 60–70 reactors by 1985. France currently has about a dozen reactors licensed to operate, about the same number under construction, and many more planned—with more than 30 new plants scheduled for construction over the next seven years. The present plan is to obtain 70 per cent of France's electricity from nuclear reactors by 1985— that's 25 per cent of the total energy consumed: 200 reactors are expected to be ordered by the year 2000.

Germany has an equally ambitious programme: two dozen reactors in operation, under construction or proposed, and plans for a further thirty or more units. Current plans envisage 35 per cent of Germany's power coming from nuclear plants.

Canada, with six plants operating, seven being built and seven more planned, seems to be the next in the Western league. Then comes Spain with three plants operating, five being built, and fifteen in all planned. Although initial plans for 11,500MW of nuclear capacity by 1987 were cut back in 1978 to 10,500MW, Spain's programme is still one of the most ambitious in Europe.

Sweden also has a major nuclear programme—five plants operating, five being built, thirteen reactors in all planned for 1985, providing half of the country's energy. Switzerland and Denmark both have three reactors operating. The poor relations in Europe are Holland (two operating), Belgium (one), and Austria with only one being built. Eire is planning just one reactor.

Argentina and Chile both have reactors operating (a small research reactor in the case of Chile—see chapter 2) while Mexico and Brazil have two units each under construction. South Africa has two reactors being built, Taiwan six, and the Philippines have plans for two. Pakistan also has two units planned, while India has three in operation and a further five being built.

The USSR has a relatively small programme—25 plants are in operation, under construction or on order: a total of 35 is expected by 1984. By comparison the USA's nuclear output is, or will be, some fifteen times larger. By 1984 Bulgaria is expected to have four units,

---

**Table 2**
Countries with Nuclear Power Reactors by 1984

| Country | Number of power reactors | Country | Number of power reactors |
|---|---|---|---|
| Argentina | 2 | Korea | 3 |
| Austria | 1 | Mexico | 2 |
| Belgium | 8 | Netherlands | 2 |
| Brazil | 3 | Pakistan | 1 |
| Bulgaria | 4 | Philippines | 1 |
| Canada | 19 | Poland | 1 |
| China | ? | Romania | 1 |
| Czechoslovakia | 5 | S. Africa | 2 |
| Finland | 4 | Spain | 18 |
| France | 38 | Sweden | 12 |
| FRG | 36 | Switzerland | 9 |
| GDR | 5 | Taiwan | 6 |
| Hungary | 2 | UK | 39 |
| India | 7 | USA | 165 |
| Iran | 4 | USSR | 35 |
| Italy | 9 | Yugoslavia | 1 |
| Japan | 32 | | |

Source: *Nuclear Engineering International*, April 1977, Supplement.

Note: Some nuclear power plants consist of two (or more) reactor units—hence, for example, the 39 reactors predicted for the UK in this table.

---

Czechoslovakia five, East Germany five, Romania, Poland and Yugoslavia one each. China has nuclear capacity but few details are available. One plant is currently under construction in Cuba and four more are planned.

France, the USA, Germany and the USSR are all operating or constructing fast breeder reactors. Indeed it has been pointed out that if, for whatever reason, Britain decides not to continue with its own fast-breeder programme, it may be possible to join with France and/or Germany in a joint EEC programme.

**Opposition to Nuclear Power**

Throughout the world, people have been opposing the development of nuclear power being proposed by governments in their name. In Germany and France this has led to violent confrontations with police and security forces, involving tens of thousands of people. In Australia there have been major demonstrations against uranium mining, in the USA a series of non-violent citizen occupations of proposed nuclear sites. In Japan nuclear power has continued to be a key political issue—while in Sweden the debate on nuclear power had a major impact on the 1976 election.

Popular concern in Britain has, so far at least, been limited. While riot police, water cannons and tear gas were being deployed on the continent, the question of expanding the nuclear programme has been debated relatively calmly. There are a number of reasons for this.

First, Britain has had a medium-scale nuclear power programme for some decades now, and whatever public anxiety there might have been has been assuaged by a relatively long period of apparently trouble-free operation. In addition, many of the existing nuclear plants are in relatively remote coastal sites: Dounreay, Windscale. Thus, there have been few siting disputes. In the USA the coastal areas where many reactors have been located are quite highly populated, as are the river-bank sites in Europe.

Then again, in Britain the need for nuclear power is less urgent. There are North Sea oil and gas for, say, thirty years and perhaps three hundred years' worth of coal. And Britain is in a very good position with regard to wave, wind and tidal power—unlike Germany which has no coastline to speak of. Not surprisingly, the German government sees nuclear power as crucial to the maintenance of the German 'economic miracle'—particularly since Germany has also become a major exporter of nuclear technology.

The United States falls somewhere between the UK and West Germany, in that it has considerable reserves of oil and coal as well as good solar power and 'ocean thermal gradient' prospects. At the same time, there exists in the US a relatively powerful environmental movement, which grew up to some extent in response to the environment chaos caused by the American free-enterprise system. In Britain, planning controls and state intervention have given at least the appearance of preventing the worst excesses of uncontrolled competition. Perhaps more subtly, issues usually emerge into the centre of politics in Britain only when they can be seen to relate to party politics and in particular when working-class or capitalist interests are clearly affected.

So far nuclear power has not been seen in this light. In the main, the doubts that have emerged in the UK have been related to environmental impact or public safety, although questions of workers' health and safety and the security problems associated with fissile material have also gradually emerged into public consciousness.

## Summary of the Environmental/Safety/Security Case against Nuclear Power

1. Civilian nuclear technology is based on materials which are the crucial ingredient of nuclear bombs. This has a number of implications.

(i) In the public mind there is a fear of nuclear explosions. However, the physics of thermal reactors (Magnox, pressurised water, SGHWR etc.) is such that this is impossible—although it *is* an outside risk with fast breeder reactors.

(ii) Similarly there is a fear of radioactive pollution, akin to fallout. Although stringent controls of routine emissions are applied by the various regulatory agencies, accidents can happen and many environmentalists are not convinced that the environmental and public health risks *are* negligible. Statistics on cancer-related deaths are difficult to assess—and it will be some years before this issue can be resolved conclusively.

(iii) Fissile material could be hijacked, however stringent the security precautions, and it is technically possible to produce a crude weapon even from civilian power-station fuel. An expansion in nuclear power—and in particular the breeder reactor— implies that larger quantities of reprocessed fuel will be in transit around the country. The security measures required could lead to infringements of civil liberties.

(See *Nuclear Prospects* in M. Flood and R. Grove-White, Friends of the Earth, 1976.)

The same security problems make the transfer of nuclear technology to underdeveloped countries difficult. Nuclear power was justified on the grounds of its potential role as an energy source for the third world—as having major export potential for the advanced countries. So far the UK has sold only two units, and the fear of proliferation of weapons-making capacity seems likely to inhibit further sales.

Other issues which have been raised include:

2. The long-term waste disposal problem, which has yet to be resolved. Small quantities of highly active wastes must be kept under controlled conditions for many centuries, and in some cases for hundreds of thousands of years. To quote the Royal Commission on Environmental Pollution (Flowers Report): '. . . we believe that a quite inadequate effort has been devoted to the problems of long-term waste management and that there should be no substantial expansion of nuclear power until the feasibility of a method of safe disposal of high level wastes for the indefinite future has been established beyond reasonable doubt.'

3. The possibility of increases in the costs of uranium, together with escalating construction costs (some the result of public demands for increased safety, and the delays caused by protracted licensing confrontations). These developments could price nuclear power out of the market—if indeed it *is* profitable even at present. There is also the fear of the growth of uranium cartels of the OPEC type.

4. The health risks faced by uranium miners (we obtain half our supplies from South Africa at present) also worry some people. Such workers are exposed to radioactive radon gas.

5. The risk faced by workers in UK processing plants—although as a consequence of the enormous (and costly) attention to health and safety in the industry, conditions appear to be good as compared with other industries. But see chapter 5.

6. Many environmentalists also argue that, in any case, nuclear power will underpin a society which is wasteful of scarce resources and which has many social failings. They look to conservation and the use of renewable energy sources to redress the ecological balance and to help us move to a 'steady-state' energy economy. Nuclear power, they argue, has no part in this.

7. And finally, some environmentalist and energy analysts argue that in any case demand for energy will not continue to increase—and that this does *not* necessarily imply frugality due to economic constraints. Rather it will be the outcome of saturation in demand for energy-using gadgets.

## The Politics of Nuclear Power

The purpose of this book is to focus specifically on the newly emerging *political* issues rather than dwell on environmental or public safety problems. This is because we believe that nuclear technology is not just an evil in itself. It reflects the society which produces it, and the goals and values of the dominant class. In this, nuclear technology is not unique. Many of the problems it raises could be illustrated with examples from other areas of technology. But it does represent in a heightened form some of the main tendencies in advanced capitalist (including state-capitalist) societies.

In capitalism, profit is clearly crucial if the economic system and the position of the ruling class in it are to be safeguarded. But safeguarding the system also implies ensuring *stability* in making profit. On occasions this means resorting to force to coerce or repress those who seek to challenge the system. More usually, it means developing organisational and technological arrangements which act as direct or indirect social controls.

Thus, production systems are designed not only to ensure maximum profit, but also to maintain control over the workforce by reducing their ability to influence the work process. Historically there has been a tendency to replace skilled labour by fixed capital and energy-intensive machinery, which cannot rebel or strike or demand more money.

The 'control' goal may, in some circumstances, actually contradict the 'profit' goal and certainly there are inbuilt contradictions in continued investment in 'labour saving' technologies. Who will consume the products? Where will the capital come from to invest in the next wave of technical development?

Nuclear technology raises these questions insistently. It is a very capital-intensive technology—a major drain on the economy, limiting opportunities for growth in other industries. As we argue in this book, its net profitability is uncertain. It seems likely to have an adverse effect on employment. There are viable, safer, cheaper, more job-creating alternatives.

The central question, then, is: why is nuclear power being forced upon us? Who benefits from it? Is it simply an economic bonanza for private-sector industrialists funded by the taxpayer? Is it the result of an unstoppable technological momentum—fuelled by the career aspirations of the nuclear scientists, engineers and associated technocrats? Is it seen as a way to maintain the status quo without having to make dangerous reforms in social and technological organisation? Is it a cloak for the further centralisation of power (both types) in society? A way of breaking the power of the coal miners? These are some of the questions which this book seeks to raise, and in some cases answer.

But critical analysis it not enough. In exploring the role nuclear power plays (or is intended to play) in maintaining the existing economic and political system, we hope to demonstrate that it is in the interests of labour both to oppose nuclear power and to fight for alternatives. The fight against nuclear technology and for the alternatives must not be left to purportedly apolitical environmentalists—who could easily provide capitalism with an 'alternative' technical fix, or justification for repressive social policies. The fight must rather be seen as part of the struggle for socialism. In saying this we are asserting that socialist society *cannot* be established simply by using the technical base developed within capitalism. The technologies developed in and for the capitalist system are designed to serve the goals of that system. That is not to say *some* may not be of use in socialist society. But we need to assess very carefully whether the existing technical means can be turned to serve socialist ends. For some people on the left, the technology developed by capitalism is the 'best currently available', although its further development is constrained by capitalist economic and social relations. Once freed from these constraints, technology can develop its full potential.

We agree with this. But that doesn't imply that it will necessarily continue along the same trajectory as that followed with capitalism. There are many possible options. Our argument is that we are not tied by a 'technological determinism', a unitary view of how society can develop. The release of technology from the constraints of capitalism would open up the political question of which technical options were most freely desirable.

Such issues can be raised now as part of the process of challenging capitalism. Which is why it is vital that organised labour realise the political and economic implications of nuclear power and play a leading role in opposing it and in fighting for the adoption of alternatives. Of course, on its own this is not sufficient. Alternative technologies might enable desirable social changes to occur, but this is not inevitable. These technologies can themselves be (and are being) co-opted to serve the interests of capitalism. So it is equally vital for the labour movement to ensure at the very least that the introduction of alternatives does not increase inequalities in society, but rather opens up opportunities for a social transformation.

# Part 1

# The political economy of nuclear power

In chapter 1 Pat Coyne argues that nuclear technology is in fact one of a rare, but presumably growing, species of technologies initially created by the state, outside of normal market conditions. He traces the troubled history of the UK nuclear programme, showing the role of the government and the general institutional context.

Mike George looks at the interlocking pattern of private ownership and control of the nuclear industry and provides us with a glimpse of the multi-nationals' reasons for promoting nuclear power.

The following chapter reminds us that, in fact, things have not gone quite according to plan for the industry: in the short term at least nuclear power may not be profitable. The final chapter then looks briefly at the policies adopted by the trade-union movement with regard to nuclear power.

**Chapter 1** *Pat Coyne*

# Nuclear power and the growth of corporatism

The history of commercial nuclear power in Britain can be divided very broadly into two periods. (1) 1945–65: the development stage, when designs were tested, prototypes built, and the institutional framework set up. (2) Post-1965, when nuclear power was seen (by some at least) as a technology capable of competing effectively with other forms of electricity generation, and one which would play an increasing role in the future.

## Development

In Britain, as elsewhere, the initial impulse was military. In the late 1940s and early 1950s a uranium factory was built at Springfields in Lancashire, a uranium enrichment plant at Capenhurst in Cheshire, and plutonium production reactors and plutonium separation plant at Windscale in Cumberland. Design work on reactors and various associated technologies was carried out right from the start by government agencies. From 1946 to 1954 the agency was the Division of Atomic Energy Production of the Ministry of Supply.

In 1954 the responsibility for all research and development of nuclear energy, military and civil was given to the newly created United Kingdom Atomic Energy Agency (UKAEA). In many ways the UKAEA is unique among British institutions. Other areas of technology are largely nationalised, such as shipbuilding and air-craft, and other industries, like fuel (apart from oil), are under state control; but there is no single instance where, from the very inception of a technology, the state has stepped in and decided, on the basis of only the most rudimentary idea of the likely scope and direction of its development, that the technology was both desirable and neces-sary and was incapable of being developed by the market. On the contrary, most of the nationalised industries were in decline when taken over and the move was in part an attempt to preserve jobs.

The UKAEA is both the only source of information on nuclear power for the government, and the developer of the technology. This duality of role has plagued the history of nuclear power in Britain.

The UKAEA has developed three different types of thermal reactor, the Magnox, the Advanced Gas-Cooled Reactor (AGR) and the Steam Generating Heavy Water Reactor (SGHWR)—more even than the USA—only to abandon each in turn. Their current favourite is a modified AGR: the American Pressurised Water Reactor (PWR) waits in the wings for the AGR II's probable demise. Furthermore, the UKAEA now argue that potential limitations in uranium supplies make it vital to develop yet another type, the Fast Breeder Reactor (FBR).

The nature of the monopoly role of the UKAEA became apparent very early. In 1955, the White Paper *A Programme for Nuclear Power* proposed a 2000MW programme based on the magnox design then being used for Calder Hall and Chapelcross power stations—hailed at the time as the world's first commercial power reactors, but actually built at the request of the military to increase plutonium production. However, the Central Electricity Authority (forerunner of the present Central Electricity Generating Board, CEGB), who would own and operate the reactors, took no part in the drafting of the White Paper and were given only a month to comment on it.

In October 1956 came Suez and a new factor, security of supply, briefly entered the debate. (It was to reappear with a vengeance after 1973.) The magnox programme was increased to 5000MW, although the 1960 White Paper conceded that nuclear power would not be competitive with oil- and coal-fired generation as early as expected. Among nuclear proponents magnox is remembered fondly, largely because it actually worked. The UKAEA is forever trotting out figures which show that the magnox stations have the highest capacity factor and produce the cheapest electricity of any in the system. What they do not say is that the capacity factors are calculated after allowing for derating (ie a reduction in the stated power production capacity) to 80% to compensate for premature corrosion of components. They do not take into account the largest magnox station, Wylfa, and do not mention that magnox was costly to build, thermodynamically inefficient, and would have to be comprehensively redesigned to take account of modern safety requirements.

What is also not mentioned is that the magnox programme displayed characteristics which were to prove disastrous for the AGR. The government was anxious to encourage 'competition' as a spur to efficiency. The nine magnox stations were built by five consortia; in order to keep them in business, orders were not allocated competitively but by a covert rota. Even this help proved too little for some, and by 1963 the number of consortia had fallen to three. In addition, the UKAEA continually fed new design information to the construction firms. As a result no one magnox station was exactly like another. In effect all nine were prototypes.

An illuminating comment on who was really running the magnox programme came from Sir Christopher Hinton, the chairman of the CEGB but also a former member of the UKAEA. Questioned in 1963 by the Select Committee on Nationalised Industries as to whether the UKAEA was guided by the requirements of the CEGB as its main clients, he replied: 'I think that their activities are guided by what they think our requirements ought to be.'

## The AGR

The magnox reactor was small, technologically conservative, used natural uranium, and operated at relatively low temperatures and power densities—all factors which contributed to its relative success but made it unsuitable for further development. The attempt to make a dramatic improvement on magnox led to the biggest technological disaster in British history, the Advanced Gas-Cooled Reactor. The disaster arose not only from technological over-ambition but also from the lack of a proper framework within which the merits of each reactor type could be objectively assessed.

The story began with the 1964 White Paper which outlined the next phase of the UK nuclear programme and called for 5000MW generating capacity over ten years. The CEGB was to invite bids for both American water-cooled reactors and British AGRs. Of the three consortia still surviving from the magnox programme, the two strongest were the English Electric Company which had a pressurised water reactor (PWR) on licence from Westinghouse and the Nuclear Power Group, with a US General Electric boiling water reactor (BWR) on licence. The third and weakest consortium, Atomic Power Constructions (APC), had suffered badly from winning and then losing the Wylfa contract. It was tightly stretched financially and technically, and had withdrawn an initial tender for Dungeness B, the first station of the new programme. Seemingly out of the running, the APC gave assistance to the UKAEA on design variations of the AGR concept. Then, at the last minute, the APC used this work as a basis for a tender for Dungeness B.

The decision, duly announced on 25 May 1965 in the House of Commons, was that the AGR had proved clearly superior to US water-cooled reactors on both technical and economic grounds. However, when the figures were published they showed that the capital costs of the AGR were £78.40 per KW against £70.86 per KW for a BWR. The factors which apparently swung the decision in favour of the AGR were fuel costs and—most importantly—the 'availability adjustment'. The AGR was expected to be available 19½ days a year longer than the BWR, and when all this was taken into account AGR running costs worked out at 0.457 d per KWh as against 0.489 per KWh for the BWR.

Eventually five AGR stations, totalling over 6000MW, were built. Delays in completion have ranged up to (at least) twelve years in the case of Dungeness B where numerous technological idiocies were perpetrated, the most monumental of which was the building of the reactor containment too small to take the reactor itself.

At current prices the capital costs of each of the AGRs will be well over £1000 million, against an estimated £418 million; but this ignores the cost of capital tied up for twelve years or more and the cost of the electricity foregone. The final cost of the current programme has been estimated at nearly £3000 million—equivalent to three Concordes.

The reasons for the AGR fiasco are many and complex. On the technical side they include the failure to foresee difficulties in scaling up 20-fold from the prototype to the commercial design; the belief that experience on magnox reactors could be translated to AGRs; corrosion problems; a combination of temperature, pressure and intense vibration leading to severe insulation problems. Recently, yet another bizarre chapter was added to the AGR saga when operator-error at one of the two stations that had actually started up, Hunterston, caused sea water to enter the reactor vessel itself. Various opinions were heard on the likely effects of the incursion but the operator, the South of Scotland Electricity Board, took the view that the reactor could start up again within a year of the accident. Given the history of AGRs, that statement could be taken (literally) with a pinch of salt.

On the institutional side problems arose from the role of the UKAEA as both technical assessor and developer of the AGR technology. It was probably too much to expect that the Authority could impartially assess its own reactor against rival American designs. Certainly one critic, R. W. Guard, concluded in 1965 that despite the much advertised expertise of the evaluating team any reader of their appraisal 'is left with no doubts about their partiality'.

Assessing costs to the third decimal place was also unwise (to put it no higher) and with hindsight appears positively surrealist. The esti-mated 7 per cent difference between the AGR and the BWR has to be set against the massive escalation of AGR costs and the point is further emphasised by the fact that on capital costs alone the BWR worked out cheaper. Only by taking into account the 'availability adjustment'—which is clearly subject to even greater uncertainty than capital costs—was the UKAEA able to support its case for the AGR.

Government must share the blame. In its desire to support 'competition' it insisted on at least three construction groups when the programme was too small to support any meaningful competitive activity. In order to ensure the survival of the groups whose existence it deemed necessary to a healthy market, the government negated the whole principle and (as with magnox) doled out AGR orders on a hardly disguised rota. Even this proved insufficient. Atomic Power Constructions, weighed down by lack of finance and technical incompetence, collapsed in 1969 and its role in Dungeness B had to be taken over by the Nuclear Power Group.

## The Commercial Connection

Up to 1970 the very small coterie of nuclear policy makers had matters almost all their own way. There was no public discussion of even the size, cost and timing of any nuclear programme, let alone a debate on the principle. Even some of those most closely connected, such as the CEGB who would own and operate the stations, and the consortia who would build them, were hardly consulted.

As the magnitude of the AGR blunders became apparent other actors came onto the stage. The results could hardly be said to be an improvement.

In August 1972 Sir Arthur Hawkins, then chairman of the CEGB, told the House of Commons Select Committee on Science and Technology that there would be a need for no more than three or four base-load stations, of which one at most would be nuclear. It appeared then to the government that even the two remaining construction groups amounted to one too many and they were merged into the National Nuclear Corporation in March 1973. Fifty per cent of the shares in NNC were to be held by GEC (chairman A. Weinstock), 35 per cent were held by other private industry, and the other 15 per cent by the UKAEA. GEC were given management responsibility.

By late 1973 it was obvious something was afoot. On 19 December, Sir Arthur Hawkins informed the astonished Select Committee that the CEGB now wished to order 32 1300MW Westinghouse PWRs over the next ten years. Brushing aside any charge of contradiction between his present evidence and that of only sixteen months earlier, he made a variety of disparaging remarks about magnox reactors, called the AGR 'a disaster we must not repeat' and dismissed the SGHWR as 'obsolete'.

Hardly surprisingly, the plan attracted a barrage of criticism and was finally rejected in favour of a much more modest programme of 4000MW of SGHWRs. In the context of the British nuclear programme—with its orders of a few giga watts at a time, its White Papers with their measured, soporific prose and their appeal to interests far higher than the merely commercial—the GEC plan seemed almost vulgar. Nuclear opponents, and even some proponents, have tended to see the whole episode as a bizarre blot on the record of a programme. However, the GEC plan represents the only realistic attempt ever made in Britain to put nuclear power on a 'sound commercial footing'. The fact that to do so would have meant a programme far beyond anything which could be justified by the actual demand for electricity was, from Weinstock's point of view, irrelevant. Once sold, the problem of operating it profitably would fall on the CEGB.

British technology was rejected on the not unreasonable grounds that it was obsolete, expensive and appeared not to work very well. The PWR was attractive for a number of reasons. According to its manufacturer, Westinghouse, it was the cheapest type of reactor. It could be largely prefabricated in a factory and lent itself to production-line methods, in striking contrast to the AGRs which had to be constructed almost entirely on-site—a process described by one engineer as watch-making on a tonnage scale. The PWR was the most common reactor type in use, had been adopted by France, Italy, Spain and Japan, and there was a real possibility of a tie-up with the French, who had announced similar ambitious plans. Since the early 1950s many words had been uttered about the possibility of British nuclear exports but the only fruits had been two small magnox reactors: to Italy in 1957 and Japan in 1959. The GEC programme, producing parts for the world's standard reactor, and with the economies of scale of a large national programme, was to be the key to a British nuclear export drive.

However, it is extremely doubtful whether the expected export bonanza would have materialised even had the GEC plan been implemented. Those countries in Western Europe and Japan which could support a substantial programme insisted that the reactors be built under licence by domestic industry. The reactor exports which have taken place—to Argentina, Brazil, South Korea, Iran—have been made for political reasons on terms far from commercial, and under conditions which appear to break the spirit if not the letter of the Non-Proliferation Treaty.

The enormous size of the GEC programme indicates the scale necessary for profitability in the nuclear business. Maurice Garner, former head of the Electricity Division of the Department of Trade and Industry (now the Department of Energy) has estimated that in order to pay back R & D and investment costs for a single reactor type, at the same time avoiding loading too much on to the costs of individual reactors, it is necessary to start building between 45GW and 100 GW of capacity within six years of proving the reactor. For comparison the total capacity of the CEGB is about 60GW. Since Britain has developed two types, proposed a third (SGHWR) only to abandon it for a heavily modified AGR, will almost certainly build at least one American PWR and is currently developing the FBR, it is evident just how far from commercial reality the nuclear business is in the UK.

Indeed, the commercial hopelessness of the British nuclear programme appears to have been acknowledged by Weinstock. Following the decision to go ahead with the two new AGRs and the deferment of any decision on the PWR until 1982 at the earliest, GEC have virtually pulled out of the National Nuclear Corporation.

## The Split Nucleus

Despite these technical and economic problems nuclear power as a concept had not been a contentious issue. The conventional wisdom was that it was a 'good thing', likely soon to be fully competitive with other forms of energy, and that governments were duty-bound to support it.

Immediately after the 1974 oil crisis it was seen as even better thing. Many governments announced massive plans for investment in nuclear plant, virtually all of it American reactors. But by this time questions were beginning to be raised. In the UK opposition came first from small independent groups—Friends of the Earth and others—and initially concentrated on safety issues such as the operational safety of reactors and dangers from radioactive pollution. Their efforts were largely responsible for politicising the debate. No longer could decisions on nuclear matters be taken by a closed coterie of individuals who largely shared the same conceptions and prejudices. As the debate developed the issues broadened and became more numerous, and the divisions deepened.

The major foci of controversy became:

*Safety:* The original issue, which now shows signs of diminishing in importance: not because the questions have been resolved but because they may well be incapable of resolution. At root the question of risk becomes a clash of ethical values.

*Economics:* A highly complex issue about which there are totally conflicting claims. The economics of nuclear power have to take into account not simply the costs of a single reactor but whole system costs—the costs of transmission, the relative rates of escalation of nuclear and fossil fuel costs, plant efficiency and utilisation factors, etc, etc.

*Necessity:* Is nuclear power necessary to the continuation of industrialised society; or would a suitable combination of existing and unconventional technologies, together with any necessary modification to life-styles, do just as well?

*Proliferation:* Would peaceful nuclear programmes lead inevitably to the acquisition of weapons by those countries which operated them? And worse, would the production of large amounts of plutonium encourage nuclear terrorism? Furthermore, would the strong measures necessary to protect plutonium lead to an increasingly authoritarian and repressive state?

*Waste disposal:* Is there any satisfactory method of disposing of radioactive reactor waste products or are we simply enjoying the nuclear fruits and leaving the detritus for posterity?

The division was not the conventional left–right split. Rather, the two camps can be divided into corporatist caucus—the believers in big government and large-scale industry, indicative planning and a strong interventionalist attitude to economic strategy—and another, much less homogeneous, group. The opponents cover virtually the whole political spectrum from anarchists and libertarian marxists, through avowedly apolitical conservation and consumerist groups, to the radical right of the Conservative party. The degree of their opposition also varies, from scepticism to total rejection.

## The Proponents

*The government:* There is fairly consistent support from the Prime Minister and the Departments of Environment and Industry. The Department of Energy appears to be less enthusiastic (see below).

*The Conservative Party*—at least in the person of its chief energy spokesman Tom King. However, the greater emphasis in current Tory thinking on market economics appears to be sowing doubts among the more radical spirits.

*The CEGB* believe that cheap nuclear electricity can help stave off the competition of gas—something which worries them greatly. The addition of a large nuclear component gives further flexibility to the switch between fuels and makes the system less vulnerable to such interruptions as miners' strikes. Had the AGR programme, together with some large oil-powered plant, been on time the effect of the 1974 miners' strike would have been much less drastic.

*The TUC:* The unions represented on the influential Fuel and Power Committee are among the nuclear super-hawks. They support the present (British) thermal reactor and also the fast breeder, and see nuclear power as essential to economic growth. See chapter 4 for further discussion.

*Industry* can probably be counted among the waverers, and certainly there will be no takers for any contract not on a cost-plus basis. Only some 20–30 per cent of the cost of a nuclear power station would go to the specifically nuclear element. For the rest, the energy source is a matter almost of indifference to the contractor. Of the nuclear element a large proportion—the fuel—would be handled by British Nuclear Fuels Ltd (BNFL) and the rest would be largely designed by the UKAEA.

There is no objective reason why private industry should favour nuclear power over other sources. In fact, given the disastrous record of those companies which have entered the nuclear field, the delays and costs involved, together with the continuing political uncertainty, there is every reason for caution.

*The UKAEA*—for obvious reasons.

## The Opponents

*Conservation and environmental pressure groups:* Obviously an umbrella label. Groups range from the Conservation Society and the Council for the Protection of Rural England, through the Town and Country Planning Association, to the Friends of the Earth. The Friends of the Earth (FoE) are probably the most influential—on account of their very active membership, energetic lobbying and media visibility. Like most environmental groups they are determinedly 'non-political' at least in the party sense, although they have increasingly moved beyond environmental issues to political and institutional issues (proliferation, employment, economics, scale bureaucracy and accountability). Even so, as a lobbying organisation FoE clearly operates within 'social democratic' consensus politics (although some of the membership may subscribe to other views).

*The libertarian left:* So far the anarchists and 'unaligned' marxists have had only minimal impact on the nuclear issue: perhaps, in part, because unlike most environmental groups they operate outside of 'consensus politics' but also because the label 'libertarian left' covers a magnitude of confusions as well as some very sound analysis. Their basic point of agreement would be a rejection of the capitalist mode of production and the desire for its replacement by something more egalitarian, decentralised and smaller in scale. Grafted on to this in many cases would be concern for environmental protection. Nuclear issues have replaced Vietnam as a central concern of disaffected youth. Certainly many of those involved in nuclear protest do so because it provides a convenient focus for what is in fact a much wider disaffection.

More recently, after some hesitation, some of the marxist parties —such as the Socialist Workers' Party and the Communist Party— have begun to take up the nuclear issues. For further discussion see chapter 9.

## Splits in the Nuclear Lobby

The coalition of interests which supported nuclear power remained intact until the very recent past, but now cracks are beginning to show.

The UKAEA no longer appear to be regarded by government (or anybody else) as the fount of all wisdom. The rot probably began in 1974 when the Authority initially recommended the SGHWR, only to argue for its rejection two years later, as the complications of the commercial design threatened to run away with costs. Energy Minister Tony Benn publicly admitted that this vacillation had cast doubt on the Authority's credibility.

Another curious incident which did the Authority little good came when they were asked by the Royal Commission on Environmental Pollution to submit estimates as to how much nuclear capacity would be installed by the end of the century. The UKAEA put forward a 'Reference Programme' of 104GW—70 per cent more than the present total installed capacity of the CEGB—33GW of it breeders. The submission attracted a barrage of criticism, some of it bordering on derision. Eventually the Authority retired in some disarray, admitting that no more than one or two breeders could be working by the year 2000 and claiming, somewhat unconvincingly, that the 'Reference Programme' was not what it seemed but really represented the limit which could be achieved with an emergency programme of nuclear development. But demand is now expected to rise much more slowly, due to a combination of slower economic growth, development of conservation measures, and the dampening effect of higher prices.

The cracks may be widened by the fact that existing CEGB coal-fired power stations are older on average than either nuclear or oil burning plants. By 1990, without further orders, the CEGB coal-burning capacity may be down to 20–25GW against the 40GW and the total coal burnt may be little more than half the present 76 million tons—which represents a hefty 62 per cent of total UK coal production. This, coupled with the National Coal Board's plan for coal which looks towards increasing output from 120 million tons to about 170 million tons by the year 2000, and North Sea gas supplies, which will reach 6000 million cubic feet a day by 1982 and may go higher if a gas-gathering pipeline is installed in the Northern sector, makes the medium-term outlook for UK energy supplies one of glut.

The Labour government is also beginning to show signs of a change in attitudes. The Department of Energy under Tony Benn has moved away from total and uncritical support to a position which while still nominally pro-nuclear is becoming increasingly equivocal. The proportion of R & D funds spent on nuclear energy has dropped from over 80 per cent in the mid 1960s to about half—most of it on the FBR— while other sources, mostly coal and the renewables—wave, wind, solar, tidal—and geothermal power are receiving significantly increased funding, although the amounts are small compared to what other countries (notably Japan and the US) are spending.

Recent evidence of the Department's thinking, the Green Paper 'Energy Policy' of February 1978, is very much more cautious on the whole question of the commitment to a nuclear economy than any previous official statement:

'We are some years from the time when we need to consider whether to embark on serious ordering on a large scale, even of thermal reactors. Before that time comes it will be important to reach a reasonable degree of public consensus on the acceptability of nuclear power. For this reason the government is encouraging a wide public debate on all the relevant issues, against a background of the fullest practicable public understanding of both the benefits and the risks involved.'

A 'debate' on the nuclear power issues began in early 1976 with a setpiece between BNFL and objectors to a Japanese waste reprocessing contract. The 'National Energy Conference' followed in June 1976, a one-day spectacular at which almost everybody who is anybody on the energy scene was invited to give a five-minute presentation of views. Since then the Department of the Environment under Peter Shore has got into the act with the Windscale Enquiry on the proposed expansion of nuclear waste reprocessing facilities, and will hold a further enquiry on the proposal to build a commercial prototype fast reactor.

Out of the National Energy Conference emerged the idea of an 'Energy Commission', a body which could provide an independent source of advice to government on energy policy. Admirable though the idea might be in principle, severe doubts over the nature of the advice likely to emanate from the Commission—at least on nuclear matters—arose when its composition was announced. Of its 22 members no less than 8 were from the fuel supply industry and 5 were trade unionists from the TUC's Fuel and Power Committee. One was from the plant manufacturing industry, one from the CBI, with only three from consumer groups; the four others included academics and politicians.

From a glance it can be seen that the commission is dominated by those involved in the supply side of industry who are also those most hawkish on nuclear power. This point appears to be confirmed from the first meeting, on 28 November 1977. There Messrs Drain (TUC), Berridge (SSEB), Hill (UKAEA), Rooke (British Gas), Pearce (Shell), Kearton (BNOC) and Chapple (TUC) all pressed for an early start to the AGR. Mr Chapple went further and stressed the need for the breeder. There appeared to be no opposition.

The Energy Commission's apparent unity of views on nuclear power is, however, likely to be shortlived, again because of the prospect of a medium term surplus of capacity in all aspects of energy production. Already the chairman of the CEGB, Sir Frank Tombs, has submitted a paper complaining bitterly of the low prices quoted to industrial gas consumers and claiming that the CEGB could cut prices by 30 per cent if it could get fuel at the same price. The representatives of both the National Coal Board and the National Union of Mineworkers are likely to be drawn in as the argument intensifies over what fuel to use for the small number of power stations to be ordered between now and 1985.

Nuclear power receives enormous political subventions—£100 million a year for the UKAEA plus an indeterminate amount from military research, government-owned and -operated fuel cycle and fuel storage facilities, and government underwriting of any accident liability in excess of £5 million, not to mention the unquantifiable benefits of a massive propaganda effort. If the nuclear industry were to fund itself normally all these costs would have to be passed on to the customer. At the very least, that would make nuclear power much more expensive. It might even mean that the nuclear programme would never have been started since some elements, like the cost of storage and final disposal, and the potential cost of an accident, have not yet been determined.

## Some Conclusions

The major premise of this chapter has been that nuclear power is in one sense unique. It is the first technology which is not the creation of market forces. Rather its development was entirely the result of political decisions. Furthermore, these decisions were not aberrations nor simply cases of bad judgement, but can be seen as resulting logically from the dominant tendency of post-1945 British politics— the drift of social democracy (a creed professed with a greater or lesser degree of fervour by the majority of the political establishment on both sides of the political divide) into a form of corporatism.

This approach to the growth of large-scale corporations has been to recognise the virtue of 'economies of scale' but to control the corporate system, at least in part, through outright nationalisation or by the formation of independent institutions like the UKAEA. Its scope includes proxy control, encouraging concentration of manufacturing industry into a few giant firms which are heavily dependent on the state for contracts, investment grants, development aids or even outright subsidies.

At the same time there has been an increasing reliance on indicative planning—the setting of macro-economic targets for various sectors of the economy. The financial and institutional pressures available to government are used to create the framework of the plan, but the actual outcome is supposed to be brought about by market forces.

With nuclear power this approach has proved an almost unqualified disaster. Early claims that nuclear electricity would be 'too cheap to meter' have been transformed to the point where the breeder in particular may be too expensive to build. The setting up of the UKAEA as judge and jury in its own case has pre-empted any debate on the need for nuclear power, led to too early and too large a commitment and to a proliferation of reactor types and designs, none of which have shown any commercial promise.

Reliance on indicative planning was not the only reason for these problems. There are a number of other factors and beliefs that have underpinned (and still continue to underpin) the nuclear programme, and which have been equally problematic.

The first was technological optimism, the belief that scientific and technological progress was more or less to be equated with social wellbeing. Coupled with this was an inherent faith that all problems admitted of a technical solution, that human factors such as judgement and morality (with the implied scope for error and immorality), were to be gradually eliminated as technology advanced and indeed that such an elimination was a 'good thing'. A further factor compounding this tendency was technological nationalism, the belief that individual countries had to pursue their own particular nuclear programme or get left behind in the march of progress. This was particularly serious in the case of Britain because, by a combination of unsatisfactory design and overwhelming US commercial might, the UK has had the worst of both commercial and technical worlds.

The second major factor was the tendency towards centralisation of electricity generation, which has been going on virtually since the beginning of the industry in the UK. Monopoly of supply in any one area is inherent in the nature of the industry. It would make no sense to have a number of suppliers competing to deliver electricity to householders. However, the monopoly mentality has been carried through to the generation of electricity, to the extent that the CEGB now operates the largest fully-connected grid in the world and has more than twice as many stations over 1000MW than any other utility. When the possibility of eventual limitations on fossil fuel supply arose it was natural, given the nature of the existing network, that some other heat source would be sought. Nuclear power, which is only economic with station sizes of 1GW and upwards (if then) was the obvious candidate. Adopting it would both confirm the wisdom of increasing centralisation and make it irreversible.

The third element was that energy consumption was thought to be directly linked to national income which in turn was a reasonably accurate measure of social welfare. A society forced to curtail its energy consumption was bound to decline. This simple equation is open to objection on three grounds:

1. Uniquely in industrial history, one resource (coal) was largely replaced by another (oil) which was both cheaper to extract and more convenient to use. The result was that the real price of energy declined from 1945 until 1973 and there was then an incentive to replace labour with energy. Further, there was correspondingly little incentive for conservation or to increase fuel efficiency. Once the price of fuel increases the energy/GDP ratio begins to fall, as conservation measures become economic.
2. The term 'energy' is itself misleading. It was borrowed from the pure world of thermodynamics. In the real, messy world, people demand not energy but fuels in a disaggregated form—electricity for TV, radio etc., petrol for cars, gas for central heating and so on. Most energy/GDP relationships are crude aggregations. They take no account of energy quality, they fail to distinguish between primary, delivered and useful energy, and they foster the illusion that one

source of energy is as good as another. In fact the change from oil to electricity would involve enormous changes, of course. The ratio of primary to delivered energy would rise by a factor of two or three—meaning more input for the same output—while the capital cost of production would rise by several orders of magnitude.

3. The analysis concentrated almost entirely on supply and largely neglected demand. Past trends were extrapolated, usually exponentially, and used to predict future consumption without much analysis of what those trends implied. They largely ignored the possibility of market saturation for domestic electrical gadgets and the results of substitution by more energy efficient technologies (eg electrification of railways). More subtly, as wealth per capita increases, disposable income is spent on goods which have an increasingly higher ratio of price to energy consumption. For example, a family invests first in space and water heating, and a cooker, all of which use a lot of energy, and then in a TV, hi-fi and other appliances which may cost as much but use less. As a result, forecasts of future energy consumption are rapidly decreasing. At least one serious forecast estimates that consumption in the year 2000 may be no greater than today's.

Summing up, nuclear power in the UK has been developed and kept alive by a combination of political will and institutional inertia. Economically it has always been seen in terms of future needs rather than present benefits, and the arguments for its necessity are open to serious doubts. It is now being deserted by its few friends with any grasp of commercial reality, and the consensus of political interests which previously sustained it shows signs of cracking.

# Ownership and control:
# the power of the multi-nationals

Despite the emphasis in the previous chapter on the state's involvement in the nuclear energy business, it would be wrong to assume that private capital is unimportant. This chapter explores some of the major private enterprise operations in this field, with an emphasis on British companies' involvements.

It is important to do so for several reasons. First, the private companies involved include some of the biggest and most socially irresponsible firms, such as GEC, Rio Tinto Zinc, McAlpines, Exxon (Esso), Gulf Oil. Second, these companies and others have been busy constructing a web of inter-connecting financial and other business interests which is significant in its own right. Third, these transnational interests are involved in selling nuclear plant and know-how to any country that can pay, whether or not it has signed the nuclear non-proliferation treaty. Fourth, a substantial amount of public money is being channelled into this business via contracts and quasi-state companies.

Table 3 on pp. 40–41 lists the major British companies in the nuclear business and some of the major European companies. A large proportion are involved in other energy technologies and may be 'hedging their bets', maintaining a substantial nuclear commitment in the expectation that nuclear power will afford enormous markets in the future.

It is notoriously difficult to obtain information about the nuclear energy business; what follows can be only a partial view.

*The National Nuclear Corporation* is a fairly recently formed conglomerate, originally with a 50% government stake, later reduced to 35%. The government stake is primarily administered through the National Enterprise Board, though not exclusively so. At the time of writing Arnold Weinstock's GEC had a 30% stake in the corporation, primarily through his Reactor Equipment company, which is itself associated with the Nuclear Power Company. Some Nuclear Power Company directors are also directors of the Nuclear Power Group (HH) Ltd, and there are joint directorships between the Nuclear Power Group and the Nuclear Power Plant Company, which is owned by C. & A. Parsons. The other 35% of the National Nuclear

Corporation is taken up by British Nuclear Associates, which itself comprises Babcock & Wilcox (34½%), Clarke Chapman (28½%), and Newarthill (half of McAlpines). The Weir Group and others make up the remaining 37%.

The Nuclear Power Company is the operating company, with GEC's Weinstock in control, although recently British Nuclear Associates (and especially Babcock & Wilcox and Northern Engineering Industries) have put pressure on Weinstock to stand down. Weinstock has been favouring the American Pressurised Water Reactor (PWR) for Britain's nuclear programme, whilst the UKAEA and British Nuclear Associates now favour the British Advanced Gas-Cooled Reactor (AGR). Weinstock's reason for supporting the PWR might conceivably have had something to do with GEC's recent deal with Westinghouse (which developed the PWR design) to build a so-called 'research reactor' in South Korea, with Wimpey's construction and financed by Kleinwort Benson. It is clear that GEC and Westinghouse saw a large export potential in the PWR, and now that Weinstock can't push it in Britain (which has around £1,300 million worth of orders in the pipeline) he is not interested in heading the National Nuclear Corporation any more. It is understandable that the other British companies involved are not very happy with Weinstock—they're obviously looking for work on the British design.

*British Nuclear Fuels Ltd (BNFL)* is a fairly new type of hybrid company. It is formally a private company, but all the share capital is public money channelled through the UKAEA. More complicated still, this publicly-owned private company has stakes in the following associated and subsidiary companies:

$\frac{1}{3}$ of United Reprocessors Gmbh ($\frac{1}{3}$ German, $\frac{1}{3}$ French)
$\frac{1}{3}$ of Nuclear Transport Ltd ($\frac{1}{3}$ German, $\frac{1}{3}$ French)
$\frac{1}{2}$ of Nukleardienst Gmbh ($\frac{1}{2}$ German)
$\frac{1}{2}$ of Combustibili Nucleari SpA ($\frac{1}{2}$ Italian)
$\frac{1}{3}$ of Centec Gmbh ($\frac{1}{3}$ German, $\frac{1}{3}$ Dutch)
$\frac{1}{3}$ of Urenco ($\frac{1}{3}$ Shell, $\frac{1}{3}$ Kewa)
100% of BNFL Enrichment Ltd

BNFL's other connections are rather more tortuous, but they include Gulf Oil, Hoechst, Bayer, Gelsenberg, General Atomic Company, Nukem, and even Rio Tinto Zinc. There is an enormously complex set of financial relations stretching across most European countries and the US. BNFL is part of this complex, most of which uses public money without a scrap of public accountability. BNFL also has an arrangement with James Fisher to make and convert ships for carrying nuclear fuels. James Fisher is connected with Fred Olsen Lines.

BNFL's involvement in the European consortium 'Urenco' has led them to make a deal with Brazil's nuclear corporation 'Nuclebras'. The German end of the joint UK-Dutch-German consortium has agreed to provide eight 12,000MW power plants plus a reprocessing plant and a uranium enrichment plant; BNFL is selling Brazil a so-called 'hex' plant, without which enrichment cannot happen. Brazil, apart from being a military dictatorship, has refused to sign the nuclear non-proliferation treaty. BNFL's other connections come about through a series of joint directorships. It has directors on the boards of the Nuclear Power Group (HH) Ltd (yet another consortium) and British Nuclear Design and Construction. The Nuclear Power Group shares directorships with the Nuclear Power Company (owned by National Nuclear Corporation), and with the Nuclear Power Plant Company which is owned by C & A Parsons.

*Fairey Engineering*, part of the now-bankrupt group recently bought up by Trafalgar House (though Fairey Engineering is under NEB control), got a contract in 1969 to build a 5MW reactor in Chile. Since the Junta took over Fairey have taken to denying the existence of the contract—which is relatively easy because construction has been completed.

Fairey have also sold reactors and reactor know-how in Brazil, Rumania and Switzerland. The Trafalgar House take-over puts Fairey nuclear interests largely in their hands. Trafalgar House owns several uranium-carrying ships in Australia.

*Babcock & Wilcox*, like *Clarke Chapman*, are in the boilermaking business. Babcock & Wilcox received a £60 million order from ESCOM in South Africa for a nuclear reactor. B & W also, through subsidiaries and associated companies, manufacture light water reactor boilers for nuclear submarines. Through its associate Babcock Fives in France, B & W is involved with the Compagnie Générale D'Electricité's (CGE) contract to manufacture high-speed neutron reactors in Iran and Indonesia. The Weir Group also works with the CGE.

Other major British companies involved in the nuclear business are listed in Table 3 on pp. 40–41.

The Anglo-American company Rio Tinto Zinc (RTZ), using finance from Charter Consolidated, has a financial and working interest in Rossing and the South West Africa Co Ltd—both involved in uranium mining in Namibia. RTZ is also a defendant for fixing prices, together with Gulf Oil, in the uranium case brought by Westinghouse in the US.

In the US, the Atomic Energy Commission (AEC) was the Federal agency created in 1946 to manage the government's wartime system of atomic research and production. Its name is now changed to the Energy Research and Development Agency (ERDA). From the beginning it was set up to protect the special interests of big business and the military. The production facilities set up under AEC/ERDA were at government expense, but operated by General Electric, Westinghouse, DuPont, Union Carbide and other major companies. The AEC was run by a five member Commission, featuring:

| | |
|---|---|
| Lewis L. Strauss— | Wall Street investment banker, financial adviser for the Rockefeller brothers. |
| John A. McCone— | sometime Director of the CIA, also on the boards of Standard Oil, IT & T. |
| Marion W. Boyer— | Vice President of Exxon. |
| Kenneth D. Nichols— | former Major General in the army, sometime chairman of Westinghouse. |
| Robert E. Hollingsworth— | head of Bechtel Corporation, now trying to take over all the uranium enrichment plants in the US. |

As far as the major nuclear businesses are concerned the same sort of interwoven financial empires exist in the US as in Britain. Exxon Nuclear is a subsidiary of Standard Oil, which itself is part of the Rockefeller empire. Exxon has major uranium deposits, is fabricating nuclear fuels etc. It has an interlocking relationship at director level with the Chase Manhattan Bank. Chase Manhattan and the First National City Bank have joint directorships with General Electric and Westinghouse. Chase Manhattan has a major stake in Southern California Edison. The First National City Bank also has a stake in Edison and joint directorships with El Paso Natural Gas Company. El Paso Natural Gas has large deposits in the First National City Bank. Gulf Oil has a major stake in Southern California Edison. The Gulf Oil subsidiary, Mellon National Bank & Trust Co has joint directorships with General Electric, Westinghouse and El Paso Natural Gas. General Atomic is a subsidiary of Gulf, and the Mellon Bank has a major investment in Union Carbide, and so on.

Overall the focus seems to be moving towards investment in

mining and fuel processing rather than reactor construction. But there clearly exists an interlocking, international nuclear-industrial complex of considerable economic significance, involving the major US energy corporations and financial institutions, together with the equivalent industrial organisations in the rest of the capitalist world. (For further discussion of the US nuclear-industrial complex see 'Nuclear power: who needs it?', *Science for the People*, Vol. VIII No. 3, May 1976.)

**Table 3**
**Major Companies in the Nuclear Energy Business**
(The list is not exhaustive)

*British companies*

| | |
|---|---|
| National Nuclear Corporation | — 35% government, 30% GEC, 35% British Nuclear Associates |
| | — links with the Nuclear Power Company, which links with REL which is wholly owned by GEC. |
| British Nuclear Associates | — 34½% Babcock & Wilcox, 28½% Clarke Chapman, plus Newarthill (McAlpines) & others |
| British Nuclear Fuels Ltd | — private company, but publicly financed primarily through the UKAEA |
| C. & A. Parsons | — majority stake in Nuclear Power Plant Co. |
| Fairey Engineering | — now under NEB control |

Vickers
Whessoe
Weir Group
Hawker Siddeley
Head Wrightson (owned by Davy International, close links with Exxon.)
Hopkinson Holdings
Stone-Platt Industries
Taylor Woodrow
Wimpey
Durrell Edgar (incorporates Gravatom, Nuclear Enterprises, Nuclear Equipment)
Tube Investments
Dewrance (owned by Dresser Industries)
Foster Wheeler
Rio Tinto Zinc (Anglo-American)

*Other European companies*

United Reprocessors ($\frac{1}{3}$ BNFL, $\frac{1}{3}$ CEA, $\frac{1}{3}$ URANIT)
KEWA (Direct Association with URENCO)
NUKEM (Direct link with RTZ)
URANIT (Consortium—Hoechst, Bayer, Nukem, Gelsenberg)
URENCO (Consortium, includes Shell & Gulf Oil)
Nukleardienst ($\frac{1}{2}$ BNFL)
Combustibili ($\frac{1}{2}$ BNFL)
CENTEC ($\frac{1}{3}$ BNFL)
Siemens

# Economic and political goals: profit or control?

As the previous two chapters have illustrated, nuclear power has been pursued in earnest for various institutional and economic reasons by both governments and the multi-nationals, usually operating in a mutually supportive role. But there have also been problems, for example in relation to the economic viability of nuclear power, and these seem to be growing.

The energy corporations have always been somewhat wary of nuclear power, suspecting that, as a new, complex technology it might not be sufficiently profitable—even given the prospect of enormous subsidies from government.

In the early days in the US, the government had to bend over backwards to entice private capital into nuclear technology. They offered tax concessions, technical support, enrichment, reprocessing, and storage facilities and arranged a limit on insurance liability of $560 million per accident. (Similar provisions exist in the UK.) At one stage they even threatened to build their own power stations if private industry did not take up the offer.

In Britain this was not necessary. A considerable portion of the industry was already under state control, subsidies were easily arranged, and profitability was of less concern, since no open market for energy existed.

But in both the US and the UK it has become increasingly impossible to ignore the escalating costs of nuclear power. Many private energy corporations in the US have abandoned nuclear power, and, like US Atomic, diversified into other more profitable fields. An estimate (in the 1960s) that there would be 2000 plants by the year 2000 has been progressively reduced—to 500 under the Ford Administration and to 350–400 under Carter.

Contracts for nuclear plants in the USA peaked at 38 in 1973 but have fallen steadily since—17 in 1974, 5 in 1975, 3 in 1976, 4 in 1977. Similar cutbacks occurred in the UK, partly as a result of an increased awareness that there would be no demand for extra capacity for many years. However, some firms like Westinghouse in the US and GEC in Britain are still in business and trying to corner the market. For although in the short term profits might be minimal, even given the promise of government subsidies, the longer-term prospects look brighter, particularly if one type of nuclear plant could be mass produced. If that were to come about, the enormous research and development costs could be recouped. Westinghouse has been able to mass-market pressurised water reactors (PWRs) at home and abroad (in France and Germany among others), while as noted earlier GEC has been trying (unsuccessfully it now seems) to convince the UK government that dozens of new plants are needed —to be constructed by GEC. Clearly, then, private capital is only concerned with large nuclear programmes. Compromise would not be attractive—it's all or nothing.

But even if nuclear power plant construction itself isn't particularly profitable, there are profits to be made at the periphery, in supplying accessories, and of course, in uranium. And beyond that, there are the long-term strategic goals of the energy monopolies.

As *Nuclear Engineering International* put it in February 1975:

'. . . the big industrial concerns have not entered the business for quick profits—indeed, most of the companies that have entered the nuclear business around the world have been shaken to their foundations by losses on early projects and few can see dramatic profits in the future. For the most part the position of the industry is that the long term direction of energy supply is going to be increasingly in the direction of nuclear power and therefore for the wellbeing of their company they must establish a foothold in this sector of the business in spite of the heavy initial costs.'

Their long-term concern is to dominate the market, maintain growth and increase control. As Alan Roberts puts it:

'the interests of the capitalist class are not to be conceived as simply the making of a fast buck. They include also the preservation of a structure which will enable the capitalist system to continue.' (*The Hazards of Nuclear Power*, Spokesman 1977)

In this, private capital has an ally in the state. Governments are concerned not only to ensure continuity of supply, but also to outflank both OPEC and the mining unions, which both in the UK and US have begun to flex their industrial muscles, having realised that the 'energy crisis' has put them in a good bargaining position. The British Treasury is known to have become strongly pro-nuclear after the 1974 miners' strike[1], while the right-wing press has argued explicitly for nuclear power as a means of decreasing the power of the NUM. Nuclear power could be a 'technical fix' for some of the government's political problems. At the same time it provides an opportunity for the further centralisation of control—a cause close to the heart of many technocrats. Because of the security problems, nuclear technology requires increased secrecy and (as Part 2 illustrates) a semi-militarised workforce. And public discussion of energy policy becomes less feasible as the nuclear component of Britain's energy supply industry expands.

Fortunately, however, this trend throws up some contradictions. Centralised systems are even more susceptible to industrial action. As nuclear power workers are relied on more and more for energy they will be in an increasingly powerful bargaining position. And white-collar technical staff are becoming more and more militant. In addition, public concern over the dangers of nuclear power has forced the government to be more, not less, open about energy policy.

### References

1  See 'Windscale: a case study in public scrutiny', Jeremy Bugler, *New Society* 27 July 1978.

# Trade union policy and nuclear power

### TUC Policy on Nuclear Power

The vast majority of British trade unions are at present firmly committed to nuclear power, in the belief that there is no other alternative and that it will underpin prosperity and job security. As the EEPTU (the electricians' and plumbers' union) put it in a paper presented to the 1977 National Energy Conference: 'The development of the British nuclear programme is essential not only to safeguard our energy supplies but also to maintain our leading world position in nuclear technology. At stake are thousands of jobs in the power engineering and construction industries . . .'

At base, this commitment rests on the belief that economic growth will be the main vehicle for the advancement of members' welfare and that nuclear power is the means of ensuring continued growth. As the TUC put it in their evidence to the Windscale Enquiry: 'Economic growth is needed to secure full employment and rising living standards . . . Economic growth requires increasing supplies of energy.' They conclude that '. . . the nuclear industry will need to be able to make a sizeable contribution to Britain's energy supplies by the late 1990s'.

This general viewpoint is further illustrated in a speech made by Frank Chapple of the EEPTU, against an anti-nuclear motion debated at the 1977 Labour Party Conference.

'In this debate there are two major camps: there are those who support motions such as the one before you, and their position is that we have suffered enough from growth and it is time to call a halt to the technological threat. We should now stand still and reflect, even if we have to reduce our standard of living. That is their position—let us make no bones about it.

'The other camp—the camp that the majority of the British trade union movement is in—says that we cannot stand still, let alone reduce our standards. We have no choice but to use growth to help us solve our problems. They pin their faith in the controlled use of technology. After all, did not the Aldermaston marchers call for the peaceful use of atomic energy?

'Neither of these groups have a monopoly of environmental or safety concern. Neither of their cases is without risk, and you have been told of the radioactive risk and the plutonium peril. But what of the peril to the world's growing millions if energy supplies run out? Death through cold, starvation, and wars of conquest for the available remaining resources. In the face of the facts that the anti-nuclear lobby have failed to refute, this picture is a very real risk indeed. In any event, if Conference carries this motion, we ought in all honesty to abandon all those resolutions which demand resources and growth.'

Chapple's views are clearly reflected in the policies of the TUC's Fuel and Power Committee, which has remained steadfastly pro-nuclear.

Leaving aside for the moment the pros and cons of the growth/energy argument (discussed in Part 2) there are a number of underlying institutional and structural reasons for this commitment on the part of the Fuel and Power Committee.

The energy supply industry, although nationalised, is beset by many internal conflicts and rivalries, with fuel pricing policy being a pawn in the game. Most unions and the TUC, have continually called for an integrated fuel policy to overcome these problems, as part of a more fully developed national energy policy. But the fact that the power engineering industry is in private hands makes this difficult. In some cases, as chapter 1 indicates, the equipment suppliers' demands shape our fuel policy; the tail wags the dog.

Inevitably trade unionists in the equipment supply firms are concerned to maintain job security, so they too can be in conflict with workers in specific parts of the energy supply system. The opportunities for 'dividing and ruling' by astute corporate leaders are legion.

The result of this situation is that it is difficult for new ideas on energy to feed through to the Fuel and Power Committee. They tend to stick with existing options, and simply ask for more of everything—coal, oil, gas and nuclear. In general, theirs is a policy of 'playing safe', but this often means that they accept very conservative estimates and arguments as to future possibilities. For example, in its evidence to the Windscale Enquiry the TUC asserted that by the year 2000 'there is little doubt that the annual level of energy production would have to be in the region of some 600 million tons of coal and equivalent', and suggested that the alternative sources (wave, solar, etc.) and conservation could be expected to contribute only 50 mtce (million tons of coal equivalent) towards this. But estimates of future energy demand have been dropping continually (with official estimates for the year 2000 down as far as 450 mtce and an estimate by the Science Policy Research Unit (SPRU) at Sussex University as low as 335 mtce) while, as Part 2 illustrates, estimates for savings from conservation and the likely contribution from alternative sources are increasing dramatically.

## Dissent from the Shop Floor

Official TUC policy has come under fire from some sections of the trade union movement—for example, from the Yorkshire miners. A number of anti-nuclear motions have been submitted by branches to trade union annual conferences—the white-collar workers' unions TASS and ASTMS for example. And NALGO, the local government officers' union, presented a strongly critical amendment to the energy motion debated at the 1977 TUC Congress which argued that:

'it would be unwise to develop too great a reliance upon nuclear power as a major energy source for the future until there is no reasonable doubt about our ability to solve the problems of
1. potential hazards to health
2. long term environmental pollution
3. security of nuclear installations and materials, and
4. the vast capital expenditure involved.'

NALGO urged Congress to ask the Secretary of State to: 'delay any firm and irrevocable decisions on future developments in the nuclear energy programme, particularly on the commercial fast breeder reactor, until there has been a realistic and informed public debate on all the issues', and to 'promote a much greater investment in research programmes dealing with methods of energy conservation and the use of other sources of energy (solar, tidal, wind, etc.) so that clear non-nuclear alternatives can be presented in the final argument'.

The main thrust of this argument was however dropped in the resultant 'composite' motion (see pp. 48–49) which was passed overwhelmingly.

At present most trade unionists who are uncertain about the advisability of expanding our nuclear commitment, are concerned with the safety aspects and the long-term storage problems—and indeed the TUC has stressed that it too feels that safety and storage problems should receive maximum attention.

But wider economic and employment issues are gradually beginning to be raised. Some of the economic issues have been discussed

# TRADES UNION CONGRESS
# BLACKPOOL 1977

---

## Composite Motion
## 15

---

### ENERGY

(Motion 107 and Amendments, 108 and 109 and
Amendments)

Congress supports the balanced development of the country's energy resources, including coal, gas and nuclear, but is concerned at the increasing rate of consumption of the currently limited stock of the world's energy resources. While welcoming the current efforts of the Government to devise an overall energy strategy, Congress is nevertheless concerned by the failure of the Secretary of State for Energy to tell the British people of the grave energy problems which both Britain and Europe face in the clearly foreseeable future. Congress instructs the General Council to press the Government to formulate a plan for energy which will not leave us dependent upon as yet unproved or undeveloped sources of energy beyond the 1980's and which will ensure that the urgent decisions which need to be taken to avoid any threat to economic expansion and standards of living are no longer unnecessarily delayed. This should include the following objectives:

(i) to promote an effective energy conservation programme; all Government policy statements and consultative documents should contain details of their energy demands and how these fit in with the overall energy strategy.

(ii) to maximise the contribution of an expanded and socially acceptable nuclear programme which is consistent with the maintenance of a safe environment in terms of solving problems of health and security which may arise.

(iii) Congress supports the construction of a full scale demonstration fast breeder reactor and further declares its support for the development of reprocessing facilities at Windscale, both as an integral part of our own nuclear programme and as a significant export of advanced technology, provided that major decisions in the nuclear programme are the subject of realistic and informed research and debate on all the issues.

(iv) Much greater investment in research programmes so that other sources of non-nuclear energy (solar, tidal, wind, etc.) can be developed.

(v) to secure the prudent use of this country's vitally important and substantial stocks of coal.

(vi) to provide full opportunities for British Industry in both the domestic and overseas markets.

(vii) to plan prices so as to allocate consumption in line with the agreed aims and intentions of the energy policy rather than as a short-term expedient.

(viii) to ensure that the British Gas Corporation and the British National Oil Corporation have effective control over the overall depletion rate of North Sea oil and gas reserves.

Moved by

Institution of Professional Civil Servants.

Seconded by

Engineers' and Managers' Association.

Supported by

Society of Post Office Executives.

National Union of General and Municipal Workers.

National and Local Government Officers' Association.

Electrical, Electronic, Telecommunication and Plumbing Union.

earlier, and the next chapter attempts to demonstrate that there are alternatives to nuclear power which can produce sufficient energy, are safer, less expensive, and more job-creating, and which will thus underpin, rather than threaten, job security and prosperity.

Obviously the trade-union movement is unlikely to reverse its long standing commitment to nuclear power overnight, but at least a start can be made. It is our hope that the analysis in this book will aid the process.

# Part 2

# Nuclear power and employment

At present the UKAEA and BNFL between them employ some 25,000 people in research, development, processing and fuel fabrication plants round the country. The nuclear power plant operators (the Central Electricity Generating Board, the South of Scotland Electricity Board) employ smaller numbers—for example around 3500 in the CEGB's eight operational nuclear plants.

But, as we have said, there are also a whole host of private construction and engineering firms which contract to the government individually and through the partly state-owned National Nuclear Corporation, and through private bodies such as British Nuclear Associates.

So overall a fairly large number of people are directly or indirectly involved with nuclear power.

This part aims to look at some of the problems they are likely to face, at the implications of further expansion of the industry and at the alternative options.

Chapter 5 briefly surveys some of the health and safety issues—illustrating the importance of independent assessment of risk acceptability by trade unionists.

In chapter 6 Roy Lewis, a lecturer in industrial relations at the London School of Economics, explores some implications of nuclear power for trade unions and industrial relations, focusing on the framework of employment in the UKAEA and British Nuclear Fuels Ltd (BNFL) and in particular on the situation at Windscale. Many of the issues he raises are equally relevant to other parts of the nuclear industry and indeed to any industry where considerations of public safety and national security are of paramount importance.

Chapter 7 looks at the general employment implications of nuclear power and at the case for a non-nuclear 'alternative' industrial strategy. Finally, there is a brief assessment of the viability of the alternative energy scenario.

**Chapter 5** *Dave Elliott*

# Nuclear power and workers' health and safety: a brief guide

The nuclear industry in the UK is proud of its safety record, and with some justification. With the exception of a fire at Windscale in 1957, there have been as yet no major accidents. However, despite the attention that has been paid to health and safety there have been regular minor incidents: for example, in 1973, 35 workers at Windscale were accidentally exposed to radioactive material although, apparently, the doses they received were within the permitted range. Contamination is a constant hazard, particularly in reprocessing operations and minor accidents are frequent.

However, it is usually difficult to demonstrate an irrefutable link between working in the nuclear industry and the subsequent development of disease. Many years may pass before cancers develop and statistical sample sizes are inevitably small. Not surprisingly, controversy rages among the experts in the field. For example, Dr Alice Stewart has claimed that cancer risks may have been under-estimated by as much as 20 times,[1] while according to another report cancer deaths between the ages 60-69 for US shipyard workers exposed to radiation are nearly 60 per cent compared with 26 per cent for non-nuclear workers and 18 per cent for the public generally.[2] On the other hand, a study (NRPB-54) by the National Radiological Protection Board, based on the medical records of employees at Windscale, could not establish any causal link between deaths and exposure to radiation. However, this study did not cover workers who had left Windscale for other jobs and has met with some criticism.[3] A much more comprehensive—and necessarily lengthy —study is underway. So it will be 10-20 years before this issue can be fully resolved.

In the meantime, the General & Municipal Workers' Union has taken British Nuclear Fuels Ltd (BNFL) to court over the deaths, allegedly resulting from contamination, of two of its members who worked at Windscale. Their widows were eventually awarded £30,000 compensation. An automatic compensation scheme—like that operating in the National Coal Board—was subsequently agreed between the union and BNFL.

Workers outside the industry may also be affected, for example, workers involved in transporting nuclear waste. In December 1976, radioactive contamination was found on an empty flask used to transport nuclear fuel rods by rail between Windscale and the Wylfa power station. BNFL commented that 'while above the accepted level they were still very low and presented no hazard to those handling the flasks or to the public'.

Similar assurances followed the derailment of a container en route to Windscale from the docks at Barrow-in-Furness. In November 1975 the local branch of Confederation of Shipbuilding and Engineering Unions (CSEU) attempted to ban the handling of nuclear waste coming in to Barrow from Japan and elsewhere. The CSEU wanted information on the likely effects of an accident to a waste container, and as to whether armed guards would be posted to Barrow docks and on the trains. Representations from the GMWU, which covers crane operators at the dock and also has members working at the Windscale plant, led to the demise of the ban.

The health and safety record of most of the other energy industries is far worse than that of the nuclear industry, at least so far. But care must be taken in making comparisons. Obviously coal-mining is more dangerous than working in a power station. But we have to add to the equation the accident and death rate associated with the mining of uranium—about half of which comes from South African mines—which exposes workers to radioactive radon gas.

Charles Kerr, writing in the Australian Magazine *New Doctor*, has attempted to make a comprehensive comparison between uranium and coal over the complete 'fuel cycle', from mining, through transport processing, use, reprocessing and waste disposals. His estimates for the likely incidence of casualties from constructing, servicing, supplying and operating one 1000MW nuclear reactor, compared with an equivalent 1000MW coal-fired station are in the range of 0.74 to 100, as against 1.2 to 25, these figures including the transport casualties and delayed deaths in both cases. So, at the top end of the range, the nuclear fuel cycle may lead to four times more casualties than the coal cycle.

Obviously such figures should be treated with caution: rival analyses have produced very different results,[4] and the fact remains that deaths in the coal mining industry in the UK continue to be in double figures annually.

But they can be reduced if mining technology is developed. 618 deaths were recorded in British mines in 1947; by 1970/71 this had been reduced to 92 as a result of mechanisation, and it has fallen since to around 50 per year. The introduction of automated mining techniques, and eventually underground coal gasification and lique-faction, could cut the death toll dramatically. It's a matter of 'social priorities'—and for the moment most of the money for Research and Development is going to nuclear power (£120 million per annum as opposed to £11 million for coal).

But despite the vast amount of resources devoted to nuclear safety there are problems in the nuclear industry. In his report on the Windscale Enquiry Mr Justice Parker commented that an exami-nation of 177 minor accidents at Windscale 'disclosed that many of them were due to comparatively simple errors in design, operating instructions or information'.

This sort of situation is, of course, common in industry generally. Throughout this book we have stressed that nuclear technology is not unique. Obviously there are many other industries with serious hazards. For example, in the chemical industry there are often risks associated with possible exposure to cancer-forming agents as dangerous as nuclear radiation. Then there is the risk of major accidents like those at Seveso and Flixborough. However, nuclear technology does present us with risks on a somewhat larger and more long-term scale. A reactor core melt-down coupled with a breaching of the containment vessel, leading to the escape of large amounts of radioactive material, could kill many more workers—and local people—than a major pit accident or petrochemical plant failure.

According to an official estimate by the UK Nuclear Installations Inspectorate, after a 'worst case' major nuclear accident there could be 'several thousand deaths within a few weeks of the accident in an area extending about 10 kilometres downwind . . .' Subsequently there could be 'some tens of thousands of cancer deaths over this area'; and there is the possibility of long-term genetic damage.[5]

Obviously the chances of a major melt-down accident are slight—but they are not insignificant. For example the 1975 Rasmussen Report (commissioned by the US Nuclear Regulatory Commission) estimated that a serious accident could be expected to occur in a light water reactor (PWR) once every 17,000 reactor years. Given, say, 1,000 reactors operating worldwide by the year 2000, that means there could be one such accident every seventeen years. Of course statistics like this are questionable—in the US, the Energy Research and Development Administration has used the same report [WASH 1400] to argue that averaged out over the whole community, the individual's chance of being killed in a nuclear accident is one in 5,000 million (assuming 100 plants). (For a detailed critique of the Rasmussen Report see 'The Risks of Nuclear Power Reactors', Union of Concerned Scientists, Boston, Mass., 1977.)

In conclusion, it would be widely accepted that nuclear power offers us a relatively clean and safe source of energy *as long as all goes well*, coupled with the threat of very rare but very serious accidents. But such an assessment ignores the as-yet unquantified, or at least disputed, environmental and safety problems and impacts occurring during the routine operation of reactors and reprocessing plants.

There is obviously a lot more to say on the topic of nuclear safety: it is currently wide open to debate. As the Windscale Enquiry illustrated, many experts feel that the bland assurances given by the authorities should be carefully reviewed and that permitted dose levels should be reduced, particularly for reprocessing workers.[6] The 'acceptability' or otherwise of risks is a matter for social, rather than technical, assessment.

This is precisely the sort of area where it is vital that trade-union-appointed health and safety representatives should get access to information on accident records, risk analyses and toxicity estimates —and work out their own conclusions and demands. Whether this is actually possible, given the security requirements of the industry and the associated limitations on disclosure of information, is discussed in detail in the next chapter.

## Some examples of major accidents in the nuclear industry

*1957, October, UK.* An inadequately briefed operative failed to carry out the correct procedures for releasing built-up energy in the Windscale Plutonium Producing Pile No. 1. Undetected for nearly two days, 150 fuel channels caught fire and burned fiercely releasing volatile fission products, including 20,000 curies of radioactive iodine, up a chimney stack. Crops over a 300 square mile area were destroyed as a precaution, and two million litres of milk were poured away.

*1961, January, USA.* The Stationary Low Power No. 1 Reactor at Idaho exploded, killing three military technicians, who had been making adjustments. Their bodies remained so radioactive that twenty days elapsed before it was safe to handle them for burial; and they had to be buried in lead-lined caskets placed in lead-lined vaults.

*1966, October, USA.* A metal plate came adrift in the core of the prototype Enrico Fermi Fast Reactor, near Detroit,

blocking the flow of liquid sodium coolant. The core over-
heated and partially melted, a full melt-down being averted
by prompt action by the staff. Mass evacuation of Detroit's
two million inhabitants, seriously contemplated at one stage,
was avoided.

*1973, September, UK.* An unexpected chemical reaction in a
reprocessing plant at Windscale led to the release of
radioactive ruthenium into the working area. Some men
failed to hear the alarm: 35 received skin and lung
contamination, although this was reported to be within
permissible levels.

*1975, March, USA.* Two electricians sealing air leaks in a
cable-spreading room under the reactor control-room at the
Browns Ferry plant in Alabama accidentally set light to the
foam rubber they were inserting—they were using a naked
candle flame to check for draughts. After some delay the fire
alarm was given, but even then the control room staff failed
to shut down the plant for a vital 16 minutes. By this time the
fire had disabled many of the emergency systems including
the Emergency Core Cooling System. A makeshift pump had
to be used to avoid over-heating and meltdown. The fire
raged for six hours before being extinguished.

*1978, August, UK.* It was disclosed that twelve workers at
the Atomic Weapons Research Establishment, Aldermaston had been contaminated by plutonium, in some
cases at twice (or more) the permissible level. Once
plutonium has been ingested, absorbed through the skin or
inhaled it is very difficult to detect. The workers involved
included three women employed to launder protective
clothing and nine AUEW members. As the AUEW
convenor put it: 'Everyone has to submit to urine samples
once a month. We thought that was sufficient and we had
confidence in the management. We are no scientists and
obviously it wasn't good enough.'

A special medical screening exercise using 'whole body
monitor' equipment revealed that some workers at
Aldermaston had high levels of plutonium in their bodies.
One of those involved—a laundry worker—had been
included in the screening exercise by mistake, having
already moved to a safe area and to work unlikely to lead

to exposure. The extent to which other workers in ostensibly 'safe' areas have been similarly affected may be revealed by the Official Enquiry that has been set up.

## References

1 See *Planning and Plutonium* (Town and Country Planning Association, 1978) for the proof of evidence Dr Stewart submitted to the Windscale Enquiry.
2 See 'Radiation Haunts Shipyard Workers', *New Scientist*, 16 March 1978.
3 See for example 'Unfair play in the nuclear numbers game', *The Guardian*, 20 October 1977.
4 See for example the UK Health and Safety Commission's report, *The Hazards of Conventional Sources of Energy*, HMSO 1978, which concluded that there might be 1.8 deaths per GW year with coal, compared with 0.25 with nuclear power. Note however that this report deals only with deaths related to accidents and not the wider health effects due to routine emissions. See also D. Rose *et al.*, 'Nuclear power—compared to what?', *American Scientist*, Vol. 64, May 1976.
5 See Health and Safety Executive, *Some aspects of the safety of nuclear installations in Great Britain*, HMSO 1976.
6 See Professor R. E. Ellis's proof of evidence to the Windscale Enquiry in *Planning and Plutonium* (Town and Country Planning Association, 1978). Professor Radford, currently chairman of the US National Academy of Sciences Committee on the Biological Effects of Ionising Radiation, claimed at the Windscale Enquiry that the current ICRP (International Commission on Radiation Protection) recommended standards were twenty or more times too permissive.

# Employment and trade union rights[1]

The employment rights argument, which this chapter will spell out in some detail, is that nuclear developments involve the sacrifice of trade union rights to the overriding needs of safety and national security. This is the underlying policy of the industry's statutes, which expressly support managerial prerogative, and of the meticulously drafted collective agreements, which contain stringent limitations on industrial action and sweeping managerial rights clauses. Safety and security considerations inevitably limit collective bargaining and the flow of information, even when industrial safety is itself a central issue of negotiation and dispute, as is increasingly likely when the Health and Safety at Work Act is fully implemented. Moreover, industrial action in the nuclear industry may be subject to unusual legal liabilities, and is likely to attract military intervention. In spite of this tight structure—and perhaps in part because of it—industrial action by nuclear workers is not uncommon, notably in the nuclear industry's heartland of Windscale.

Of no less importance than the collective rights of trade unions are the civil liberties of individual workers. It is sometimes said, by lawyers especially, that workers agree or consent to the surrender of their civil liberties by taking up security-sensitive employments. In reality, class and educational background and (above all) limited job opportunities determine that 'choice'. At present nuclear employment involves a great deal of secret security activity and a corresponding restriction on civil liberties; every move towards the plutonium economy must widen the ambit of restriction.

## Collective Bargaining

The UKAEA has a statutory duty to seek consultations with appropriate organisations in order to make agreements for (a) the settlement by negotiation of terms and conditions of employment, including provision for arbitration in default of settlement, and (b) the encouragement of industrial safety and health and, 'so far as in the opinion of the Authority considerations of national security permit', the discussion of 'other matters of mutual interest', including efficiency. Almost identical provisions apply to BNFL. Two aspects stand out: first, the legislative insistence on arbitration, which is perhaps explained by the example of similar provisions in the nationalisation statutes, and secondly, the support for management's interpretation of national security.

The negotiation arrangements for UKAEA and BNFL are distinct and separate, though there are many common features. Within each organisation, there are separate arrangements for non-industrial staff (the majority at UKAEA) and for industrials, who are the majority at BNFL. As UKAEA was created largely from establishments under direct civil service control the national and local negotiating machinery for non-industrials is still based on the Whitley committee system, the staff are members of civil service unions, and the terms and conditions including pay and gradings are settled by reference to the civil service. There is little opportunity therefore for tough collective bargaining.

For industrial employees the civil service negotiating link was severed. Both UKAEA and BNFL have national and local level joint industrial councils, composed of representatives from the two sides and including some shop stewards at national level. Agreed procedures cover disputes, discipline, safety and check-off, and there is comprehensive provision for shop stewards' committees, facilities and delegate conferences. BNFL have a post-entry closed shop arrangement, and there is virtually a closed shop in the UKAEA. In the light of the statutory duties of UKAEA and BNFL, there are express safeguards for management's view of national security as well as arbitration clauses. It is important to note that, though the statutes provide for the conclusion of procedural arrangements and the promotion of health and safety and make discussion of 'other matters' alone subject to management's interpretation of national security, in fact the collective agreements go further and expressly make all joint deliberations subject to management's overriding view of security. The arbitration clauses are invoked on a fairly regular basis, especially for conflicts of interpretation, and are declared in the agreements to be 'binding' on the collective parties and on the members of the recognised unions.

At the time of writing UKAEA's agreed no-strike clause reads: 'There shall be no stoppage of work, withdrawal of labour or closure while any negotiations are in operation or pending, and no negotiations shall take place during the period of any such stoppage, withdrawal or closure'. BNFL's equivalent clause says simply: 'There shall be no stoppage of work, withdrawal of labour or closure while any negotiations are in operation or pending'. BNFL has recently negotiated a general no-strike obligation in the context of a limited status quo clause, as well as a further strike restriction to cover inter-union disputes.

## Industrial Conflict

This comprehensive structure of statutory and collectively agreed rules, as well as the need to maintain safety and national security, would suggest peaceful industrial relations, if not the 'remarkably good record of industrial relations' claimed for BNFL by its managing director during the Windscale enquiry. For non-industrial employees, peace appears to prevail, apart from some sporadic participation in general civil service protests against government pay or public expenditure policies. But for industrial workers the situation is different, and even a cursory examination of press cuttings indicates that nuclear workers resorted to industrial action on several occasions during the 1970s.

In 1972 UKAEA employees demanding danger money blacked a key building at the Atomic Weapons Research Establishment, Aldermaston. In 1974 industrial grades staged a one-day official strike throughout UKAEA establishments in pursuit of a pay claim and parity with BNFL, and there was a related strike threat at BNFL's Salwick plant. At the same plant, in 1975, canteen girls struck against a proposed reduction in bonus payments, and that led to a sympathy strike by all industrial grades who were concerned about bonus payments generally. The most severe industrial unrest has been at Windscale: a ten-day unofficial stoppage in 1973, a fireman's strike in 1976, and a seven-week unofficial stoppage between January and March 1977. This last strike raised many sensitive issues. The analysis of it which follows is based on research conducted by the Socialist Environment and Resources Association (SERA), who interviewed a number of workers involved in the dispute, newspaper reports, and on transcripts of evidence from the Windscale enquiry. Substantially the same account was given in SERA's evidence to the enquiry, where it was not challenged by BNFL.

Windscale is a large establishment with a labour force of some 4,500 of whom approximately 3,000 are manual workers. It is engaged in a productive process rather than in laboratory work, and there were several outstanding pay and productivity issues. Attempts had been made to introduce incentive schemes, but, in the face of employee opposition based on safety considerations, these were withdrawn and the bonus payments consolidated. However, suspicion remained about future management plans on incentives. In general, the workforce favoured improvements which would bring them in line with the petrochemical industry, and a more specific demand was for increased special pay for certain types of work, especially that carried out in accepted 'high risk' areas. In other industries such payments would be called 'danger money', but in the nuclear industry they are officially regarded as payments to reflect a high degree of responsibility and care. The agreements provide an 'abnormal conditions allowance' payable to certain workers who are liable to require decontamination from exposure to radiation, and other special payments include an 'irksome duty' allowance to compensate for the wearing of protective clothing. There is also a lump sum payment to compensate workers who are for medical reasons permanently taken off plutonium-related shifts.[2]

It was clear that industrial safety was a critical issue in BNFL's industrial relations. Although the nuclear industry claims to have a good safety record, it is officially recognised that the storage and reprocessing of nuclear fuel necessarily exposes workers to radiation; another acknowledged problem is the difficulty of disposing of contaminated protective clothing.[3]

Persistent anxiety at Windscale over safety found expression in monetary demands, perhaps because of the difficulties of eliminating the risks, and certainly the pay structure reflected the inherent dangers of nuclear employment. It was known that the trade unions were supporting claims for damages against BNFL in respect of deceased employees, on grounds that radiation had caused their deaths.[4] Moreover, the stewards considered that all radiation-induced sickness should be classified as an industrial disease for the purposes of compensation. Also widespread was the belief that fuel rods at Windscale tended to remain in reactors for six months longer than the design specifications allowed, rendering the cladding fragile and highly irradiated. Finally, management was suspected of secretiveness over safety issues and this festered further mistrust.

Early in 1977 a pay dispute developed among locker-room workers. As handlers of the 'irksome' clothing, they received half the 'irksome' allowance and, having claimed the full amount, they struck unofficially. A large proportion of the industrial workers were immediately laid off by BNFL. This was regarded as extremely provocative, and a plant-wide unofficial strike in breach of procedure was called shortly afterwards, an overall pay increase becoming the principal demand. The rapid escalation of the dispute took the full-time trade union officers by surprise (as it did BNFL), and official recommendations to return to work were rejected by the strikers. Fears were raised about the safety of the plant and some attempts were made to pass safety materials and chemicals through the picket line. These fears increased and by the fifth and sixth weeks pressures to end the strike were intensified. The Health and Safety Executive, the TUC and the Secretary of State for Energy (Tony Benn) were involved in assessing the risks and persuading the strikers to return to work. The workforce was aware of moves to use troops to bring in safety equipment, and the possible use of the 1875 Conspiracy and Protection of Property Act was raised as an issue. At length, the pickets consented to the delivery of materials; troops were not used for that purpose. In making this decision the strikers, according to BNFL's managing director, 'did draw back from the brink', and the chairman of the official union side agreed that the safety aspects of the strike had been 'an exercise in brinkmanship'. Shortly afterwards, the strike was over. The settlement gave an across-the-board abnormal conditions allowance of two-and-a-half pence per hour, a small amount in view of the long duration of the strike, and in November 1977 locker-room workers were again threatening to withdraw their labour.

It was, however, agreed that the adequacy of the settlement would be determined by an arbitrator. In the arbitration hearing, the union side claimed a substantial increase over the previous two-and-a-half pence settlement in order to compensate for an alleged deterioration in conditions caused by (a) increased levels of radiation contamination; (b) increased security activity which produced new levels of inconvenience and embarrassment; and (c) increased public interest in activities at Windscale with consequent psychological pressures on workers and their families. Management rejected the radiation argument, and also the security activity argument, though it did acknowledge that security measures had been tightened in consequence 'of the increase in violence in society in general and of the increase in the vehemence of the statements made by anti-nuclear extremists'. The psychological pressure argument was conceded as reflecting a marginal deterioration in conditions. In the event, the arbitrator awarded a further two-and-a-half pence increase on the abnormal conditions allowance.

**Right to Strike**

During the course of the Windscale Enquiry the inspector, Mr Justice Parker, asked the TUC for their opinion on whether the law ought to restrict strike action in the nuclear industry. The TUC's reply expressed concern for safety in a nuclear strike but opposed legal restrictions, emphasising instead the need for negotiators 'to draw up agreed rules' on safety which would apply in a dispute. The correspondence seemed to ignore the problem of what happens when strikers and managers disagree, as they did during the Windscale strike, on whether or not safety is an issue at all. Moreover, there is also the question of the extent to which existing laws might restrict industrial action. For example, the freedom to picket peacefully in a trade dispute (Trade Union and Labour Relations Act, section 15) does not give a legal right to stop lorries, a point which might have become an issue in the Windscale strike. This is a problem of general labour law and not one peculiarly associated with nuclear disputes. But there are three areas of restriction which, though having a wider relevance, are particularly applicable to the circumstances of the nuclear industry: the Conspiracy and Protection of Property Act, civil liability based on criminal offences, and the use of troops.

Nuclear disputes with a serious safety implication fall within the potential ambit of section 5 of the Conspiracy and Protection of Property Act 1875. This section states: 'Where any person wilfully and maliciously breaks a contract of service or of hiring, knowing or having reasonable cause to believe that the probable consequences of his so doing, either alone or in combination with others, will be to endanger human life, or cause serious bodily injury, or to expose valuable property whether real or personal to destruction or serious injury, he shall on conviction thereof . . . be liable to pay a penalty not exceeding £20, or to be imprisoned for a term not exceeding three months . . .'. Although there appears to be no record of any prosecution under section 5, the possibility might encourage employees to give notice to terminate their contracts of employment before embarking on industrial action, though that was not a feature of the dispute we have described. Beyond that, the section has a very wide scope; according to the Donovan Report 'section 5 applies to both parties to a contract of service, and not merely to the employee. An employer who broke an obligation on his part under a contract of service and thereby provoked a stoppage of work having the probable consequences specified in the section might be criminally liable thereunder'. Might that include a precipitate lay-off of the kind that was exemplified in the Windscale dispute?

In discussing this measure it is acknowledged that general legal rights concerning union organisation, collective bargaining and industrial action are restricted in certain highly exceptional cases; for example, in respect of the armed forces and of merchant seamen. But the trade union movement has always opposed such restrictions and the tendency has been to downgrade them. For example, the Industrial Relations Act 1971 repealed section 4 of the Conspiracy and Protection of Property Act 1875, which had specified criminal liability for some breaches of employment contracts in the gas, water and electricity industries. The government has introduced the Post Office Workers (Industrial Action) Bill, 1978, to cut down the legal restrictions on the rights of postal workers to engage in industrial action, and the legal restraints on trade unionism within the police force, contained now in the Police Act 1964, are under challenge. But so long as section 5 of the 1875 Act remains on the statute book, it may give rise to criminal liability in a future nuclear dispute.

Industrial action in the nuclear industry might also lead to criminal liabilities under the various statutes which regulate nuclear safety, or, perhaps more remotely, under the Official Secrets Acts 1911–1939. The commission of these offences, as well as breach of section 5 of the 1875 Act, points to a further possibility, namely, civil liability. If nuclear workers broke statutory obligations specifying only *criminal* sanctions, that could still lead to *civil* liability which would not be protected by the Trade Union and Labour Relations Act. Moreover, *Gouriet*'s case (the action instigated in 1977 by NAFF against the Post Office trade unions to restrain them from boycotting South African mail), whilst denying to members of the public the right to bring a civil action based on breach of the criminal law (in the absence of a special interest or special damage), nevertheless confirmed the Attorney-General's discretion either to bring such an action himself or allow what lawyers call a 'relator' action. An Attorney-General might regard a civil injunction as a suitable means of restraining industrial action in the nuclear industry; and should an injunction be flouted, as might happen in an unofficial dispute, proceedings for contempt would ensue.

The possible use of troops was an important aspect of the Windscale strike. Troop manoeuvres in the vicinity of the plant were part of the persuasion to return to work. The general role of the military in civil affairs appears to be increasing and contingency planning to meet internal emergencies has been stepped up, partly as a result of the five proclamations of emergency arising from industrial disputes during the period of Conservative government, 1970–74.[5] Troops may be deployed in industrial disputes under regulations following a proclamation of emergency, where it appears to the government that 'there have occurred, or are about to occur, events of such a nature as to be calculated, by interfering with the supply and distribution of food, water, fuel, or light, or with the means of locomotion, to deprive the community . . . of the essentials of life . . .' (Emergency Powers Act 1920, amended by the Emergency Powers Act 1964).[6] This definition is applicable to nuclear disputes which interfere with 'fuel' or 'light', as in the Windscale

65

strike, which severely disrupted BNFL's sales of electricity. It may still be argued that the deployment of troops does not restrict industrial action as such, and moreover, that the 1920 Act expressly debars the regulations from instituting compulsory military service for strikers and from making it an offence to strike or persuade others to do so. But the actual or threatened use of troops may decisively affect the balance of industrial power.

Both the proclamation and the regulations are subject to review by parliament. However, the Emergency Powers Act 1946 made Defence Regulations of 1939 permanent and allowed the armed services to be used without proclamation or consultation with parliament 'on urgent work of national importance'. Members of the armed forces (in theory, like other citizens) are also under an obligation to act, if need be with necessary force, in aid of the civil power on request. The request may come from the Home Secretary, and not the magistracy as in the past: a point confirmed in 1976 by the Home Secretary, who blandly viewed parliament's power to dismiss him or reduce his salary as 'complete parliamentary control' over his actions. The state, moreover, retains a still more obscure prerogative to direct the use of troops. Whatever the precise legal authority, there have been several recent examples of the use of troops in industrial disputes without emergency proclamations.[7] Certainly, a government faced by a nuclear strike and concerned for safety or security would have ample power to use troops, even if the dispute fell outside the terms of the 1920 Act.

### Bargaining, Security and Safety

The arbitration claim described above illustrates how the effect of national security procedures may become a subject of collective dispute. National security inevitably impinges on collective bargaining and, as we have seen, the Atomic Energy Authority Acts of 1954 and 1971, and, more particularly, the collective agreements, permit negotiation only insofar as management's view of national security allows. A similar constraint must apply to disclosure of information, including the legal duty of employers under the Employment Protection Act to disclose information to trade union representatives for collective bargaining. This is consistent with the exemption in the Act's disclosure provisions for information 'the disclosure of which would be against the interests of national security', and a security certificate signed by or on behalf of a minister automatically debars a claim for particular information.

The pervasive preoccupation with national security in the nuclear industry may encourage a more general management secretiveness over many areas, including safety, which appeared to be part of the background to the Windscale strike. Thus, despite the existence of joint safety committees, shop stewards in 1976 found it necessary to publicise their anxiety about BNFL's concealment of information on the seriousness of a radioactive leak at Windscale.

The problem will doubtless become more acute from October 1978 when section 2 of the Health and Safety at Work Act, together with Regulations, a Code and Guidance Notes are brought into force.[8] Section 2 requires employers to consult with the safety representatives of recognised trade unions and, if requested, to establish joint safety committees. The Regulations specify a number of functions for representatives and committees including the carrying out of inspections, monitoring hazards and safety information, and liaising with the inspectorate. How far will national security override these requirements? The Regulations excuse the employer from the duty to give safety representatives 'any information the disclosure of which would be against the interests of national security'. An example of such information is provided by the arrangements for the manufacture, storage and transport of plutonium.[9] Moreover, national security is likely to vitiate the operation of the Code of Practice, which specifies that safety representatives ought to be given information on the plans and performance of the undertaking, and proposed changes as well as information affecting safety 'of a technical nature' in respect of 'machinery, plant, equipment, processes, systems of work and substances in use at work. . .'.

The role of the Nuclear Installations Inspectorate also merits comment. Under the Nuclear Installations Acts 1965 and 1969 and the Health and Safety at Work Act, the nuclear inspectorate, which is now under the Health and Safety Executive of the Health and Safety Commission, is involved in the design and construction of nuclear plant as well as in the monitoring of prescribed standards for the protection of the environment and community and of the employees. The authoritative Flowers Report[10] on nuclear power and the environment had 'doubts about whether the criteria adopted by the . . . [inspectorate] . . . in establishing reactor safety are soundly based and whether their functions are correctly defined' (para. 282), and went on to recommend the establishment of an additional, more independent advisory body. This recommendation and the reasons behind it were accepted by the government in its White Paper in response to the Flowers Report.[11] Nevertheless, the Health and Safety at Work Act imposes new and important duties on the nuclear inspectorate (along with all other inspectors) in relation to employees.

Section 28(8) requires inspectors to give adequate safety and health information to employees or their representatives; where safety representatives are appointed, they are to be the appropriate persons to receive the information and generally to consult with inspectors. In assessing how the relationship between the nuclear inspectorate and trade-union safety representatives might develop, one must add to the considerations of national security, which are likely to impede the relationship, the additional factor that this particular branch of HSE is required by its statutory duties to maintain an unusually close working relationship with management, a tendency which can only be strengthened by any future development of a commercial fast breeder reactor. As fellow nuclear experts, moreover, the inspectorate have a great deal in common with the scientific staff of UKAEA and BNFL, and, whether conscious or unconscious, a high degree of identification with management is likely. For example, in the aftermath of the Windscale strike, the inspectorate regarded it as a normal part of their duties to assist BNFL in devising methods of eliminating reliance on the supplies which the pickets had been able to block. This assessment is reinforced by the extraordinary action of the nuclear inspectorate's clerical staff who, in February 1977, through their branch of the CPSA, demanded the full publication of the inspectorate's data from a health inquiry on BNFL employees, due to the 'feeling that official reassurances do not meet the facts'.

## Workers and Civil Liberties

Just as collective relationships are affected by the needs of national security, so are the liberties of individual workers. The Official Secrets Acts 1911–39 apply to the nuclear industry, and the Nuclear Installations Act 1965 specifically empowers the state to issue national security directives, which may require that a person be not admitted to employment or that their employment be terminated. Moreover, a complaint of unfair dismissal fails if the dismissal is made 'for the purpose of safeguarding national security'. A minister's certificate is conclusive evidence on national security; similarly, a request for particular information in an unfair dismissal claim will be refused on grounds of national security on the provision of a certificate.

In addition, and consistent with the Official Secrets Acts, UKAEA's and BNFL's conditions of employment expressly prohibit the communication of any information in the course of employment to any person without proper authority, or the giving of such information to newspapers, or the publication or broadcasting of any matter relating to employment without the employer's prior written consent. Other security aspects were raised by the Flowers Report, which pointed out that 'the security risks are long-term and likely to become increasingly severe', especially if there is a substantial growth in nuclear power and a move into the 'plutonium economy'. Flowers identified three problems: (a) infliction of deliberate damage to nuclear installations by terrorist sabotage or enemy action; (b) theft of plutonium, and the possibility that it could be made into a bomb or otherwise dispersed into the environment; and (c) whether security arrangements to counter these dangers might jeopardise civil liberties.

The workforce 'will require to be screened before being employed, as they already are, and they may be subject to unusual surveillance during the course of their employment'. There is also the 'secret surveillance' of those 'who may make "undesirable" contacts. The activities might include the use of informers, infiltrators, wire-tapping, checking on bank accounts and the opening of mail . . . We regard such activities as highly likely, and indeed inevitable'. During the course of the Windscale Enquiry, BNFL effectively confirmed the on-going nature of the kind of employee vetting and secret surveillance described by Flowers. The vetting process covers the ethnic, religious, and moral background of job applicants and employees, their political and trade-union activities, and perhaps also their attitude towards nuclear power. Trade union officials concerned with the industry are no doubt similarly vetted.

Another aspect on which Flowers shared the public 'disquiet' was the Atomic Energy Authority (Special Constables) Act 1976. In order to strengthen the protection of material such as plutonium in transit, and of certain installations, including Windscale, this Act conferred powers on the Atomic Energy Authority's special constabulary to carry firearms, engage in hot pursuit and arrest on suspicion. This puts the industry's security personnel on the same footing as the Ministry of Defence constabulary, which is a unique arrangement in civil employment. A final and related matter, which concerned Flowers, was the official action that would be necessary in the event of plutonium theft or nuclear blackmail. It would include general search warrants (which are at present illegal), enforced evacuation of threatened areas, restrictions on the right of movement and assembly, and the suspension of habeas corpus.

In the aftermath of the Flowers Report the Department of Energy issued an extraordinary press notice (Long Term Security of Nuclear Power, 2 June 1977). This announced that surveillance in the context of nuclear power would extend only to bodies and individuals where there is reason to believe that their activities are 'subversive, violent or otherwise unlawful'. There is no crime of 'subversion' known to English law, though according to a government minister the operational definition is 'activities threatening the safety or wellbeing of the state and intended to undermine or overthrow parliamentary democracy by political, industrial or violent means'. 'Under that head' said Justice, a group of lawyers concerned with civil liberties, 'authority could easily—and secretly —be given for the surveillance of individuals or bodies having political, religious or philosophic views or beliefs of which the government of the day happens to disapprove, though there may be nothing unlawful about those views or beliefs, or the activities of those who hold them'.

**Conclusion**

Employment and trade union rights are today upheld by a legislative policy which favours collective bargaining as the preferred method of regulating employment relations, and recognises that the peaceful manifestations of industrial conflict are an essential ingredient of the bargaining process. This public policy was succinctly restated by the Scarman Report on the Grunwick dispute: 'In our judgment, good industrial relations depend upon a willingness to co-operate and compromise. The law favours collective bargaining and encourages the use by workers of independent trade unions for the purpose. The policy of the law is to exclude "trade disputes" from judicial review by the courts and to rely not on the compulsory processes of the law but on the voluntary approach backed by advice, conciliation and arbitration to promote good industrial relations. The efficacy of such a law depends upon goodwill.' It also depends on the mutual responsibility and self-discipline derived from the exercise of the freedoms to organise, to negotiate and to resort to industrial action, which are central pillars in Britain's unwritten constitution. In the nuclear industry, these freedoms and the laws which support them are in jeopardy.

Nuclear disputes may lead to civil sanctions based on criminal offences, or, more directly, to criminal sanctions on either workers or managers. Such legal intervention would no doubt exacerbate a strike. Military intervention is also a possibility. This could entail technological risks, damage industrial relations, and would tend towards authoritarianism. Yet industrial unrest has occurred despite the existence of restrictive laws and a highly organised and formal structure of management-trade union relationships, which at Windscale has been unable to contain or even anticipate unofficial disputes. This suggests a tension between the official institutions and the shop floor, which is not unusual in British industrial relations, but is disturbing in the nuclear industry because of its inherent dangers. However, attempts to domesticate the unofficial element, whether through existing or new laws (compulsory arbitration and removal of the freedom to strike, for example) or even by tightly-drawn agreed rules, could prove to be a dangerous course. Prior to the development of collective bargaining and the various peaceful methods of industrial struggle, industrial conflict commonly found expression in riot, violence and machine-wrecking. If the freedom to engage in organised and peaceful strikes and picketing is further restricted, there is a danger that individual or group dissatisfaction would culminate in acts of sabotage, which might have devastating effects in the nuclear industry.[12]

This perspective ought to be a warning to those who might be tempted to conclude that nuclear employment warrants exceptional restrictions on industrial action. It also underlines the paradoxical industrial strength of nuclear workers: if they engage in industrial action their bargaining power is potentially greater than any other group, including the miners, yet their formal collective rights under legislation or agreements is severely limited, partly by the possibility of criminal sanctions and the use of troops, but especially by the overriding concern for protecting national security.

National security pervades and limits the collective relationship and must inhibit moves towards extending industrial democracy, whether by way of collective bargaining, wider disclosure of information, planning agreements or reconstituted boards. This applies to the question of industrial safety, which is a most sensitive subject in nuclear employment, notwithstanding the tendency for anxiety over safety to find expression in economic demands and concessions. At a time when full employee-participation in safety is the policy of parliament and industry, nuclear employment must frustrate that policy in important respects.

Finally, the needs of national security restrict the liberties of individual employees. The very procedures for dealing with security risks offend against freedom of opinion, and, being secret, are open to mistake or abuse. They are also open to political interference and manipulation,[13] but are manifestly not subject to any meaningful democratic political control. This latter point was driven home when the Flowers Report was belatedly debated in December 1977 in the House of Commons on a motion by a private member, Leo Abse, who aptly described the White Paper in response to Flowers as 'formal and bland' and anticipated a 'dusty answer' for any MP who sought to probe the operation of the security service; to which the Energy Minister replied: 'I can give only the classic answer—that I am advised that the increase in surveillance and vetting will not go above a normal level.' It should be emphasised that the full range of secret security measures is already deployed in respect of existing employees, a process which must expand if we move towards the plutonium economy.

Nuclear employment involves major inroads on employment and trade union rights. Where a systematic curtailment of these rights begins, it is not easy to know where it is going to end. These are matters of fundamental importance, which ought to be weighed in the balance of argument about the future development of the nuclear industry.

## The TUC on Nuclear Safety, Security and Trade Union Rights

The TUC in its submission to the Windscale Enquiry supported the proposed expansion of reprocessing facilities, but pointed out that 'restriction on trade union rights of disclosure of information and the accompanying security and secrecy arrangements already exist for those trade unionists in UKAEA and BNFL sites'. For example, 'Under Regulation 7(2)a of the forthcoming Safety Representatives and Safety Committee Regulations, trade-union-appointed safety representatives would not be allowed access to health and safety information or details of hazards and accidents or to their members' workplaces if the disclosures of these would be against the interests of national security'. It is not clear precisely how the TUC expect this problem to be resolved. In a somewhat opaque sentence they suggest that 'trade union safety representatives appointed under the Safety Regulations having met relevant security requirements should have access to health and safety information details of hazards and accidents and access to their members' workplaces'. Does this mean special screening of the safety reps. before they are appointed, or is the TUC simply pointing out that all workers at BNFL are vetted when appointed in any case? As regards strikes the TUC felt that the unions and BNFL should discuss and agree on 'steps which must be taken to protect the plant and the

community if a dispute develops', through the Joint
Industrial Council.

Whether an agreement can be arrived at that would
preserve nuclear workers' rights to strike and picket
effectively or whether, as one witness at the enquiry
advocated, they will ultimately be denied such rights, as are
the police and armed services, remains to be seen.

D.E.

### The Windscale Enquiry: Report by Mr Justice Parker, March 1978

In the final report, the inspector presented the following
analysis of the interaction between safety and the right to
strike—an analysis which in no way resolved the problems
raised above.

'One objector expressed strong views that the safety of the
public demanded that the workforce at Windscale should
give up, and be proud to give up, the right to strike, in
exchange for terms and conditions guaranteed equal to the
best in equivalent posts in industry generally. Any disputes
should, he thought, be dealt with by arbitration and the
arbitration award should be binding. He considered that the
workforce would thus become an elite workforce.

'The objector concerned was a Mr W. C. Robertson. He had
himself worked at Windscale, is a fellow of the Institution of
Electrical Engineers and had had very considerable
experience in electrical and mechanical engineering.
Bearing in mind that published newspaper reports of the
strike, which had occurred at Windscale early in 1977, had
suggested that the point of danger to the public had been
very closely approached as a result of the strike, it appeared
to me necessary, not only to explore the possible
consequences of a strike but also to seek the views of Mr
Adams (as representing local workers), the TUC and BNFL on
the suggestions made by Mr Robertson.

'BNFL, the TUC and Mr Adams were at one regarding
restrictions on the right to strike as being unnecessary. All
took the view that whilst there would have to be agreed
procedures to ensure that a strike would not endanger the
public such procedures would be sufficient. No doubt this

would be true if it were possible to ensure (a) that there could be no disagreement about the point at which public safety became overriding and (b) that the workforce on strike would always comply with the procedure agreed. Neither is possible. It is commonplace to find that there is disagreement about the imminence of danger and equally commonplace to find that men on strike do not follow their leaders' advice or directions.

'If, therefore, it had appeared to me that the absence of the workforce or a part of it would be likely to create significant hazards I should have had no hesitation in endorsing Mr Robertson's suggestions. Having investigated the matter I do not consider that it is likely provided that picketing in aid of a strike does not prevent either: (a) delivery of essential supplies or (b) the attendance without hindrance of a small safety force to maintain surveillance and take any remedial action necessary in the event of e.g. the failure of one source of electric or water supply.

'Even if it does the public can no doubt be protected, as was pointed out in the 1977 strike, by the use of troops unless the situation is such that special expertise is required from them. This does not, however, provide a particularly reassuring answer to the public. There is always a reluctance to employ troops until their employment is absolutely unavoidable. This reluctance is due to the escalation of the dispute which is likely to follow upon the use of troops. This being so there is necessarily a possibility that there may be a misjudgment as to the moment when their use can be held off no longer.

'This matter is not peculiar to the THORP facility on the site, or to Windscale, or indeed to the nuclear industry. It is not appropriate that I should make any recommendation. Having, however, heard evidence from a number of local witnesses I have no doubt that the local public would be greatly relieved if they knew for certain that no matter what industrial action was taking place there would be no hindrance to the delivery of essential supplies or to the attendance of a safety staff on site.'

Insofar as the report does discuss the civil liberties of workers and the right to strike, it exhibits a strong right-wing bias.

While the report cites the TUC in support of nuclear power,

and the union side of BNFL's negotiating machinery in
support of the company's safety record, the proposal raised
at the enquiry for a wider compensation scheme for workers
suffering from radiation was flatly rejected, as was any
suggestion that the nuclear inspectorate serve the interest
of the industry rather than that of the employees or the
public. A non-nuclear policy, according to a key passage of
the report, would entail the danger of a greater dependence
on coal and 'on those whose co-operation is required for its
exploitation than presently exists'. In short, we have the
normal establishment and judicial bias against militant
working-class organisation and miners in particular.

As for the civil liberties issue, that also involved a very
grave danger. Without adducing any evidence, the report
painted a spectre of people 'with evil purposes' seeking to
overthrow the system and commented 'it was plainly
possible that the aim of doing harm can be pursued under
the outward guise of furthering such a worthy aim as the
protection of civil liberties. A campaign to lessen
surveillance, ostensibly to preserve civil liberties, could
therefore be mounted by people whose aim was not the
preservation of such liberties but increased opportunity to
further their own destructive ends'. Consistent with this
conspiracy theory, the inspector had insisted throughout the
enquiry that discussion and evidence on security and civil
liberties be kept to a general level, for fear of providing
terrorists with valuable information. Nevertheless, in view of
the concern of bodies such as Justice and the Council for the
Protection of Rural England, the inspector was constrained
to recommend that an independent body should vet and
review security measures. This weak proposal merely
confirmed the report's remarkable admission that there is
indeed no solution to the problem of civil liberties in the
nuclear industry.

Given this treatment of the civil liberties argument, the
question of industry action was seen purely as a possible
threat to public safety. Had the inspector considered this
danger to be acute he would have had 'no hesitation' in
recommending new laws to restrict strike action by nuclear
workers. However, as the extract indicates, he did not think
that this was necessary in view of the reserve power to use
troops, and providing that picketing did not hinder the
attendance of safety staff or the delivery of essential

supplies. Blocking supplies was of course a major weapon in the 1977 strike. What the report seems to be saying—although Parker avoids spelling it out—is that nuclear workers ought to forego their industrial strength through an agreed procedure, and if they refuse, then new laws might be necessary.

R.L.

### References

1 Roy Lewis gave evidence at the Windscale Enquiry for the Socialist Environment and Resources Association; much of this chapter is based on his more detailed article 'Nuclear Power and Employment Rights', *Industrial Law Journal*, March 1978.
2 Certain nuclear workers who are exposed to radiation are covered by the Employment Protection Act's sections on paid suspension from employment on medical grounds: ss. 29–33 and schd. 2.
3 HSE *Nuclear Establishments 1975–76*, HMSO 1978, especially paras. 121–132 (radiation), and 88–102 (disposal of protective clothing).
4 BNFL has subsequently agreed on £30,000 compensation plus costs in settlement of two of the claims, in one of which liability was admitted. *Guardian*, 16 November 1977.
5 See Adam Roberts, 'The British armed forces and politics: a historical perspective', *Armed Forces and Society*, Vol. 3, no. 4, August 1977; Tony Bunyan, *The Political Police in Britain*, Julian Friedmann 1977; Carol Ackroyd *et al.*, *The Technology of Political Control*, Penguin 1977.
6 Industrial disputes have led to eleven proclamations of emergency, in some of which troops have been used: 1921 (miners), 1926 (miners and general strike), 1948 (dockers), 1949 (dockers), 1965 (railwaymen), 1966 (merchant seamen), 1970 (electricity supply workers), 1970 (dockers), 1972 (miners), 1972 (dockers) and 1973–74 (miners).
7 Glasgow dustmen, 1975; civil air traffic control assistants, 1977 (use of RAF to supply strategic radar stations, despite pickets: *Financial Times*, 14 October 1977), firemen, 1977–78.
8 The Safety Representatives and Safety Committee Regulations, 1977, S.I. 500. On the Code and Guidance Notes, see *Safety Representatives and Safety Committees*, Health and Safety Commission, 1976.
9 The government refuses to answer parliamentary questions on specific plutonium movements. See M. Flood and R. Grove-White, *Nuclear Prospects: A Comment on the Individual, the State and Nuclear Power*, Friends of the Earth, 1967, p. 7, citing relevant passages from *Hansard*.
10 Royal Commission on Environmental Pollution, Sixth Report, *Nuclear Power and the Environment*, 1976, Cmnd. 6618 (the 'Flowers' Report).
11 *Nuclear Power and the Environment*, 1977, Cmnd. 6820, para. 29. Subsequently the Advisory Committee on the Safety of Nuclear Installations has been set up to advise the Health and Safety Commission.

12 Research suggests that individual conflict manifestations may increase as industrial action declines. See R. Hyman, *Strikes*, Fontana 1972, pp. 53–56.

13 For example, a recent factory occupation led to the discovery that employees of a British Steel Corporation subsidiary were politically vetted on behalf of management, not only by Special Branch, but by the Economic League as well. *The Guardian*, 23 May 1977.

**Chapter 7** *Mike George and Dave Elliott*

# Jobs, energy and industrial strategy

The modes of production, distribution and exchange of energy reflect and reinforce both the existing economic relations in society and the underlying ideological assumptions which operate in society. In this chapter we look in detail at some of these assumptions, and particularly at those which underpin the trade-union movement's current commitment to nuclear power.

A key assumption is that growth in employment is linked to energy growth. At first glance this seems to make sense—more energy production means more jobs in power stations, more jobs in building generating equipment, and more jobs in the industries that use the energy. But at the same time it is also clear that in fact, energy- (and capital-) intensive machines have been developed and used to replace labour. So more energy does not necessarily mean more jobs. Indeed, it can means the reverse.

To illustrate this, let's look first at the energy-generating industry itself—where power stations are becoming ever more capital-intensive and output is increasing, but employment is falling.

## The Energy Supply Industry

In his book *The Fissile Society* Walt Patterson notes that 'The electricity supply is the most capital-intensive industrial sector in the British economy. As at 31 March 1976 the net assets employed by the Electricity Council and its Boards in England and Wales amounted to £5991 million. The number of employees totalled 166,826. On average, therefore, the industry employed £35,912 worth of assets per employee. The CEGB itself is yet more capital-intensive. At 31 March 1976 it was employing 63,212 people and net assets of £3697 million—£58,485 per employee.'

He adds: 'comparison with the figures for 1967 is revealing. In the decade 1967–76 total employment in the electricity industry in England and Wales dropped from 228,520 to 166,826 a decrease of 27 per cent. In the CEGB total employment dropped from 80,189 to 63,212, a decrease of 21 per cent. During the same decade the number of units of electricity sold to customers in England and Wales increased from 141,418 million to 189,458 million, an increase of 34 per cent . . . In the entire industry in England and Wales, Council plus Boards, 55,269 industrial jobs disappeared, in the CEGB alone the lost industrial jobs totalled 16,669.'

These job losses are in part a result of increased investment in new technology and in particular, the move to larger, marginally more efficient plant, coupled with the acceptance by unions of productivity ideals.

## The Power Station Construction and Power Engineering Industry

But even though fewer workers are needed to produce power due to increased productivity and the use of more efficient technology, surely jobs will be created in the power engineering firms which build power station equipment? But while building power stations is bound to create some employment, the numbers employed in this industry have fallen in recent years—for example at Reyrolle Parsons, from 8437 in 1963 to 5104 in 1973.[1]

There are a number of reasons for this. As is discussed later, overall demand for energy has not risen as fast as expected, and Britain has now 40 per cent or more excess capacity. No new plants will be required for a decade or more. This is the result of the large ordering and construction programme of the last couple of decades—based in the main on large power plants, which tend to generate fewer jobs in boiler-making, turbogenerator manufacturing and civil engineering than programmes based on larger numbers of small plants: the latter programmes are more flexible and work can be spread over a wider range of firms.

As Patterson comments in *The Fissile Society*: '. . . a single order for a single large unit can only be allocated to one plant. When it is completed, the large workforce involved in its construction must obtain another order or be laid off. The official response to this dilemma is to encourage new construction schemes and new orders as fast as necessary to maintain employment.'

While it is vital to maintain employment—more than 30,000 jobs are at stake—given the reduced levels of energy demand, this policy, resting as it does on continued ordering of new plants, is not a long-term solution. Unless a new approach is adopted, mergers, contraction and redundancies are inevitable.

Although the current situation owes much to over-ordering, recession and the increase in oil prices since 1973, it is also clear that the private power-engineering companies have seized the opportunity to increase profits by rationalisation.

In the long term, the net effect of rationalisation, technological

**Diagram 1:** Unemployed 1963–1977, Great Britain

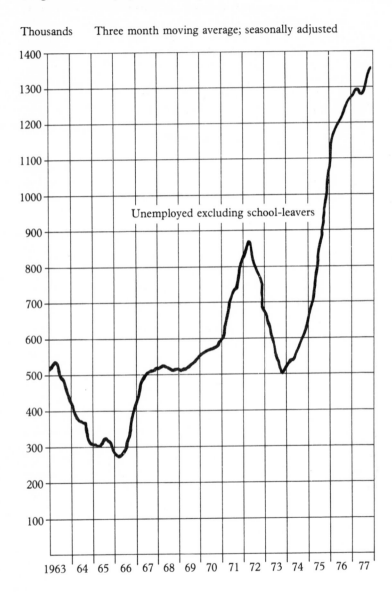

Thousands    Three month moving average; seasonally adjusted

Source: Department of Employment

change and productivity increases will be that Britain's energy demands will be met with less labour.

## Energy Use in Industry

But even though we may be able to produce energy with fewer generation and construction workers, surely the energy produced will support employment *elsewhere* in the rest of the industry? Unfortunately this does not seem to be the case—at least not over time. What happens, in many cases, is that energy is used to power new labour-saving devices: energy replaces workers. Productivity is increased (which in itself is desirable), but this is attained at the expense of labour. Note that it is not technological progress that is being criticised here. The use of energy to reduce arduous work is obviously sensible. Rather we are criticising the specific form of technological development that is introduced under capitalism: technology which reflects the goals of those in power in society and which has many adverse social effects. Structural unemployment is one of the most dramatic outcomes.

The unemployment that has spread through western society in recent years is a result not only of the latest 'cyclical' economic recession, which some economists believe will eventually lift, but also a consequence of cumulative job losses due to the introduction of new labour-saving technologies, such as mechanisation and automation in the production sector and electronic data-processing and computers in clerical work.

Diagram 1 illustrates that, historically, after each previous 'slump' fewer workers were taken up when the 'boom' came: structural unemployment is increasing as more capital is invested in labour-saving devices—a trend which is not only affecting manufacturing industry, but also the service sector.[2]

In some cases the use of electronic control systems, automation and so on may result in energy saving and the efficiency of use of energy in industry may increase (it already has in the steel industry). But in general, this simply means that replacing workers is even more attractive in economic terms. At present most types of mechanisation involve a net increase in energy consumption and as Table 4 below shows, despite reduction in coal consumption, energy use in industry has increased continuously (at least until the 1973/74 oil crisis), while employment declined by nearly 1 million in the decade 1968–78 in the manufacturing industries.

To sum up: Growth in energy availability and use through increased investment in advanced energy technology does not necessarily create jobs in the energy supply industry or in the industries supplied with power. Like investment in capital-intensive technology generally, it is more likely to reduce employment.

**Diagram 2**

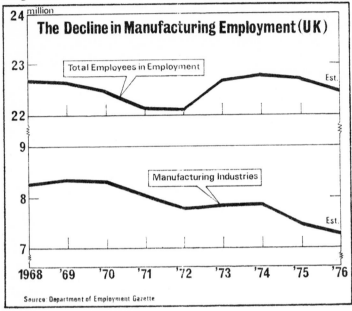

**The Decline in Manufacturing Employment (UK)**

**Table 4**
UK energy consumption by industry 1950–1975
(in billion therms) ie equivalent heat supplied

|  | 1950 | 1960 | 1970 | 1975 |
|---|---|---|---|---|
| Electricity | 0.7 | 1.5 | 2.5 | 2.6 |
| Oil | 1.7 | 4.5 | 11.4 | 8.8 (post-oil crisis) |
| Gas | 0.9 | 1.5 | 1.9 | 5.5 |
| Solid fuel | 15.7 | 13.9 | 8.9 | 5.0 |
| **Total** | **18.9** | **21.4** | **24.7** | **21.9** |

Source: 'UK energy supply and demand prospects' National Energy Conference Department of Energy, 1977.

*Note to Table 4*

It is not suggested that there is necessarily a causal link between job losses and energy consumption in industry. Recently there has been a downturn in energy consumption while unemployment has continued to increase. But these statistics should serve to illustrate that in our present economic context and with the existing type of technology, increased energy consumption does not, as often claimed, necessarily increase employment.

Obviously in the historical sense, during the early phase of industrialisation, the use of energy in industry led to growth in output and economic growth generally. But at some point within the development of technology a point is reached when there are no further net gains in employment. A detailed study of the relevant 'production function' for the various industries concerned would be required in order to find out at precisely what stage of capitalisation this point is reached.

For a detailed analysis of trends in energy consumption in industry, see 'Estimating energy demand for the year 2000', Science Policy Research Unit, University of Sussex, February 1978. The diagram on page 84 is abstracted from this. It indicates that while in some sectors energy use per unit output has risen, in most it has fallen—there is clearly no simple positive correlation between energy input and production output.

For further discussion see *The Potential for Substituting Manpower for Energy*, G. Reday and W. Staher (1977), Battelle Memorial Institute, Geneva Research Centre; produced for the Social Affairs Division of the Commission of the European Communities.

## Economic Growth and Energy Growth

Yet the belief that growth in energy production inevitably leads to employment remains dominant among many politicians, businessmen and trade-union leaders. To some extent this is because we have gone through a lengthy period of relatively full employment, when both energy consumption and the economy were growing—a fact which has led observers to infer a causal link. For example, in this country in the years 1950 to 1973 overall growth was matched, and more than matched, by a growth in energy production and consumption—and, at least up to the mid-1960s, full employment was maintained.

But the relationship between energy, economic growth and employment has gradually been altering. As we have already noted, the increase in output has been achieved in part by the introduction of new *technology* (whether energy-saving or energy-using) which has tended to produce structural unemployment. Those who still believe in the existence of a direct link between energy demand and GNP take no account of the type of technology adopted and, in particular, the efficiency with which energy is generated and used. For example France, which has a higher GNP per capita than the

**Diagram 3:** Trends in Energy Use Per Unit of Output in Manufacturing Industry

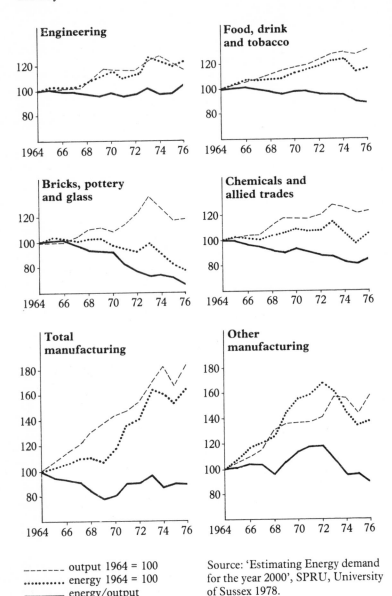

---------- output 1964 = 100
•••••••••• energy 1964 = 100
━━━━━━ energy/output

Source: 'Estimating Energy demand for the year 2000', SPRU, University of Sussex 1978.

**Diagram 4:** International Comparison of Primary Energy Utilisation

Tons of oil equivalent
per year per capita

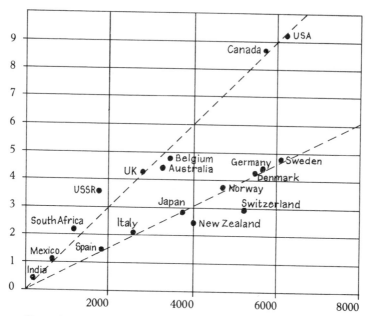

Gross domestic product—dollars per capita

Source: *UN Statistical Yearbook*—taken from p.171, Proceedings of the Institute of Mechanical Engineers, Vol. 190, 30/76.

Note to the above graph: The UK is on the 'high energy use' line, whilst countries such as Germany and Sweden enjoy a much higher standard of living (or at least a high GDP) without using as much energy per capita as that used in the UK.

Obviously there are a great many reasons for some countries having a more efficient use of energy in relation to living standards, but the graph suggests that energy saving or conservation would not *necessarily* result in lower living standards—Italy as a whole has similar living standards, but energy consumption is around half that of the UK.

Facts such as this need to be carefully scrutinised by those who argue that individual and national economic wellbeing depends on a high and growing consumption of energy—just how can Denmark use the same energy per capita as the UK, but sustain a standard of living which is higher?

UK, consumes only half the primary energy consumed in the UK. This is largely due to the comparatively greater use of electricity in the UK.

The increase in oil prices (and hence all other primary fuel prices) has however led to a move away from the wasteful use of electricity in such applications as space heating. Britain's energy needs seem likely in future to be met by more efficient means—with the result that the projected growth in energy consumption in the UK has been declining.

This is not the place for an extensive analysis of the vagaries of energy forecasting and the failures of the energy planners.[3] But the fact is that demand for electricity has not increased as the planners believed it would. The Department of Energy has just had to revise its forecasts for demand by the turn of the century downwards by 20–30 per cent (roughly equivalent, note, to the size of the energy gap of 100 mtce that is supposed to open up in the 1990s), and estimates are continually dropping (see Table 5 below). It may well be that demand will remain more or less static at its present level.

---

**Table 5**
Some official estimates for energy demand by 2000 (in mtce) current consumption 342 mtce:

| June 1976 | 420–760 mtce | (Energy Research and Development in the United Kingdom) |
| June 1977 | 500–650 mtce | (Energy Policy Review) |
| October 1977 | 450–560 mtce | (Working Document on Energy Policy) |

*Note:* The (1978) report by the Science Policy Research Unit at the University of Sussex referred to earlier suggests that consumption by the year 2000 may be as low as 335 mtce ('Estimating UK Energy Demand for the year 2000').

---

## The Costs of Nuclear Power

Although these sorts of arguments are beginning to have an impact, in the main the energy institutions still insist that there's an enormous need for more energy, and that nuclear power is the only way to meet the so-called 'Energy Gap' which, they continue to predict, will occur towards the end of this century. They paint pictures of economic decline, restricted use of electricity, mass hypothermia and civil unrest. It could almost be said that life as we know it depends on ever-increasing energy consumption. And they say that means nuclear power. But not just the good old thermal reactors we know and love. Uranium will become increasingly scarce. What we need, they say, is the fast breeder reactor which (given time) can stretch our uranium supplies by a factor of 40, by breeding plutonium from otherwise useless uranium 238.

Quite apart from the associated safety and proliferation hazards, the fast breeder nuclear reactor programme is likely to swallow up huge amounts of capital. Exact cost figures are notoriously difficult to obtain in this security-conscious industry, but it is estimated that the proposed British prototype commercial fast breeder reactor will cost in the region of £2 billion. This reactor is supposed to supply about 100 megawatts (MW) of electricity, and we are supposed to need about 40 gigawatts (GW) of nuclear energy by the year 2000. This will cost in the region of £80 billion—around 5 per cent of Britain's gross domestic product until then.

And it could cost more—if the nuclear proponents have their way. The UKAEA proposal (submitted in evidence to the 1976 Royal Commission on Environmental Pollution) was for the provision of 104GW of nuclear capacity by the year 2000, a programme which could cost £150 billion and would need an investment equivalent to about 10 per cent of the gross national product. Such programmes could well starve investment in other sectors of the economy.

This is a problem even for relatively rich countries like the USA. As Barry Commoner argues (see below) there is a real prospect of overall capital starvation if the US embarks on large-scale capital intensive projects such as a major nuclear power programme. Even some high Tories are put off the nuclear option by the enormously high capital costs; the nuclear option could mean yet more IMF loans, and that means continuing incomes policies and public expenditure cuts. All this in the name of economic growth.


Capital Starvation

In *The Poverty of Power* (Cape, 1976) Barry Commoner argues that the *US* energy industry is facing capital starvation on account of the escalating capital cost of ever more complex technologies—nuclear power plants being the most extreme example. Despite charging consumers more for their energy, the industry complains that it cannot maintain sufficient return on capital invested in power plants to support ever-increasing demand for capital to invest in new plant. Now to some extent this might be 'special pleading' by companies keen to receive larger government handouts but it is clear that few firms want to invest in power plant construction, preferring other more profitable areas of investment. As the chairman of the Edison Electric Institute put it in 1974: 'it is impossible in present circumstances to build a power plant that will yield a satisfactory return on investment'.

Commoner argues that this is a result of a general trend: 'For every dollar invested in energy production in 1960, 2,250,000 BTU of energy was produced, by 1970 this figure had dropped to 2,168,000 and in 1973 to 1,845,000—an 18 per cent decrease in the productivity of capital in energy production in only thirteen years. (These figures are cited in terms of 1973 dollars to eliminate the effect of inflation.) Between 1970 and 1973 the capital needed to support energy production amounted to about 24 per cent of the capital invested in US business as a whole. Estimates of the capital needed to produce energy in the 1975–85 period range up to $1000 billion, and are likely to demand a third or more of the total capital needed by private business.'

If the private energy companies are unable or unwilling to meet these demands from their own internal funds where *will* the money come from? Well, the state is the obvious source—and that means the taxpayer. But there are obviously limits to what can be obtained in this way during a recession.

The other possible source is of course speculative investment of savings by private individuals, insurance companies, pension funds and so on. But, says Commoner, according to an analysis produced by the US Stock Exchange, 'even the considerably increased reliance on such external funds will not meet industry's total need for capital in the next ten years'.

Who would want to invest in an industry whose rate of return is falling? Property and commodity speculation is far more attractive. What Commoner is describing is the fundamental contradiction of the capitalist economic system, resulting from the substitution of capital for labour.

*Business Week*'s analysis of the 'Capital Crisis' pointed to an overall investment capital need for US industry as a whole of $4500 billion over the next decade and commented: 'the obstacles to raising that kind of money in the economic environment that is likely to prevail in the next decade and distributing it to where it will be needed, are formidable, perhaps insurmountable'.

## Jobs and Energy in the USA

Several US commentators have pointed to the fact that investing in energy supply technology is a poor way of creating jobs. Dr John Holdren told the US Sub-Committee reviewing the National Breeder Reactor Programme in 1975: 'The energy producing industries comprise the most capital-intensive and least labour-intensive sector of the US economy'.

A study based on data from *Fortune* magazine indicated that in 1975 the top 15 oil (energy) companies tied up 21 per cent of all available capital, but provided only 4.5 per cent of all the jobs, in the top 500 corporations. More jobs could be created by spending money on almost anything else.

For example, another US study indicates that every dollar's worth of electricity takes 502,473 BTU to produce and deliver but provides only 0.04363 jobs compared with social service activities (eg welfare services) at 27,791 BTU and 0.086365 jobs, and hospitals 26,121 BTU and 0.17189 jobs. Manufacturing is in-between energy production and the services industries in terms of energy intensity (eg automobile manufacture 55,603 BTU) and jobs created (0.07754 jobs).

## Employment in Nuclear Power

In the energy production and distributing industries themselves there is, as we have seen, a continuing trend towards larger and larger plants with fewer and fewer workers. The apex of this trend is of course the nuclear energy industry. The expanded nuclear reprocessing facilities at Windscale have a projected cost of over £600 million, but only 1000 or so new jobs would be created (many of those are in construction which are short-term only), which puts the 'cost' of each new job created at over £600,000. The 'cost' of creating new jobs in the proposed expansion of nuclear energy as a whole is similarly high.

According to a study carried out by the Energy Centre, Newcastle University for the UKAEA, the increase in employment resulting from a programme of the type proposed by the UKAEA to the Flowers Commission might be as follows:

|                        | 1980   | 1990   | 2000    |
| ---------------------- | ------ | ------ | ------- |
| Admin/technical staff  | 9,733  | 16,421 | 23,201  |
| Scientists/ engineers  | 6,707  | 16,731 | 28,934  |
| Skilled                | 8,321  | 32,560 | 59,511  |
| Other                  | 11,538 | 32,361 | 61,540  |
| **Total**              | 36,299 | 98,343 | 173,186 |

This assessment includes research and development, construction, operation and maintenance, but ignores transmission and the design staff requirements of the National Power Company.

If we include component manufacturers (the above figures include turbine generator manufacture etc. but omit some other components) the figure rises to a total of about 200,000 jobs in the industry in the year 2000. (Figures from the Watt Committee on Energy Report No. 2 'Deployment of National Resources in the Provision of Energy in the UK 1975–2025'; August 1977. Available from the Institute of Mechanical Engineers, London.)

If this figure seems a significant employment gain, it is one achieved at enormous expense. Comparing different energy industries' capital inputs and employment, the picture looks dramatically different:

| Industry           | Capital input per annum | Numbers employed | Capital input per job |
| ------------------ | ----------------------- | ---------------- | --------------------- |
| Coal mining        | £200m                   | 250,000          | £800                  |
| Gas and oil        | £400m                   | 200,000          | £2,000                |
| Electricity boards | £800m                   | 150,000          | £5,000                |
| Nuclear energy     | £4,000m                 | 200,000 [2000]   | £20,000               |

The figures are approximations but they indicate the order of difference between the energy industries. In fact the £20,000 'cost' per job in the nuclear industry is vastly under-rated, for only 3500 or so new jobs will be created in it in each year up to the year 2000. On this basis, each new job created will have a capital cost of around £1 million!

The composition of nuclear energy workforce is also different to that in the other energy-producing industries: white-collar staffs form over 40 per cent of the total labour force, and many of the workers in the 'other' category would be on construction work with short-term jobs only.

The Watt Committee Report (1977) concluded that it would be relatively easy to obtain the necessary numbers of scientists and technicians for the industry, and there would be no problems in recruiting 'other' staff—construction workers, unskilled, security etc. But the demand for skilled workers would outstrip supply, so it is expected that some workers would be recruited from other engineering industries. This is obviously an undesirable step for it would channel scarce skills into an unnecessary and extremely capital-intensive industry. However, the report placed emphasis on expected increases in productivity in the nuclear industry, and concluded that 'reasonable' increases would reduce the workforce necessary from 200,000 to 80,000, with only 800 or so skilled workers needed each year.

So, on the one hand the industry could poach skilled workers from other industries, and on the other there would be work for only around 25,000 skilled workers by the year 2000, with 800 or so being recruited each year—neither effect seems to be desirable, bearing in mind the enormous capital investment in the industry.

Summing up so far: Britain uses energy wastefully compared with other countries—it is assumed we carry on using it wastefully—we therefore have to pay a high energy price for our economic and industrial activities.

It is assumed that general economic growth is desirable—it is assumed that a lot more energy is needed to support and encourage this growth.

It is assumed that there will soon be an 'Energy Gap'—the only way to fill it is to use large amounts of nuclear energy—but nuclear energy is very capital-intensive—the costs of building and operating large-scale nuclear industries could adversely affect resources needed for economic growth. It is assumed that increasing economic and energy consumption growth will help provide employment—but nuclear energy creates very few jobs in relation to capital invested.

Nuclear energy is not the miraculous 'cheap' energy of the future;

it is costly and brings in train a host of undesirable effects. But what are the alternatives? First we should look at the ways in which we consume energy.


## Cutting Waste

Our energy consumption depends totally on how our society works. Consider for instance the amount of oil wasted in the market economy. One lorry passes another on a motorway; both carry almost identical biscuits, one takes them from Glasgow to London, the other from London to Glasgow. Another example might be found in housing. At the moment we use about 29 per cent of our primary energy in the domestic sector for house heating, etc., most of which goes out of the windows or through the roof; yet a very ordinary sort of insulation programme could save about half of this: 15 per cent of our total energy consumption. And even moderate improvements in energy efficiency by industry would have saved more power than all the nuclear power stations have produced since they started.

It would need a very detailed study to show how we could modify our industries and homes in order to achieve the higher energy efficiencies of countries such as Sweden and Germany. But quite simple measures like housing insulation can bring great benefits. Rather than 'allowing' old-age pensioners to avoid paying enormous electricity bills, is it not more desirable to provide well-insulated homes with minimal heating bills? Heating insulation programmes are also labour-intensive and could provide new jobs at a 'cost' of a few thousand pounds. For example, a full-scale programme designed to insulate all the 19 million houses in Britain would cost £1,800 million and could create around 12,000 jobs over ten years. Induced and indirect jobs would also be created in the materials industries.

The market economy means that the poor tend to buy cheap electric fires rather than central heating for their homes, yet the operating costs of cheap electric fires can be three times as high as the costs of gas central heating. Overall, electrical heating is the least efficient form of space heating, yet millions of homes in this country rely on it, whilst the moneyed class invest in more efficient forms of heating. Not only would government-sponsored insulation programmes lower our energy demands substantially; they would also provide an important social benefit. In addition, there would be an employment benefit for the construction and materials-supply industries.

This really brings to light the need to look at what is termed the 'end use function' of energy, its use-value. We use energy for motive power, for heating, for cooling, for electronic circuits and so on. Quite a large part is used for space and water heating, and much of this heating uses electricity, yet only 15 per cent or so of our total energy needs have to be met by electricity (about 40 per cent of total energy supplied is electricity). So what the energy institutions are proposing is an enormously costly nuclear power programme to produce a type of energy which is inappropriate for a wide range of applications.

If we look further into the use-value of energy it becomes clear that we need to relate forms of energy and types of energy generation much more closely to everyday uses. If we look at conventional modern power stations, we see expensive oil being used to create steam to drive turbines to produce electricity. Sixty per cent of total energy input is lost through waste heat, more is lost through the transmission lines, and the final efficiency of a one-bar electric fire in an uninsulated house would be laughable, if it weren't so serious. The same points apply to a nuclear power station; it's an expensive way of raising steam, much of which pours out of cooling towers or ends up heating rivers or the sea.

The price of centralised electricity generation through oil, coal or nuclear power stations is bound to increase, and the overall efficiency of the system will remain ridiculously low (30 per cent at best). But there are several ways of increasing the efficiency of our power stations. We have a large number of unused or under-used small urban power stations that have been phased out in favour of very large oil-fired 'sets'. These small sets are suitable for recommissioning as *combined heat and power* units. Rather than be rejected into the environment as at present, the waste heat from these stations can be used in local district heating networks (as was the case in Battersea). This would raise the efficiency of the system considerably (from 30 per cent to over 60 per cent) and would avoid the absurdity of converting heat into electricity, then converting this into heat again.

Such a recommissioning programme is eminently sensible during a period of energy glut and would bring large employment gains. The stations would be more labour-intensive than the large sets, and would provide work for a vast range of skilled workers in the design and implementation of district heating schemes. There would also be a demand for new generating equipment.

A new type of coal-burning technology has been developed, which would be well suited to this type of plant. The *fluidised-bed* system basically burns granulated coal which is heated to a very high temperature and kept agitated by large gas flows. This means a much higher thermal efficiency—much more heat is obtained from a ton of coal than in conventional coal-fired sets—and the more efficient combustion means less pollution. Domestic waste can also be burnt.

## Alternative Energy Sources
Some of the so-called alternative energy sources are quite feasible propositions for the near future. As the next chapter indicates, solar power systems could make a major contribution to domestic and industrial space and water heating; and given sufficient funding, wave- and wind-power systems could be important in electricity generation.

The employment gains from developing these energy sources are difficult to quantify, but a US study by Laitner indicated that per unit energy a solar power programme would by the year 2000 create 2.5 times more jobs than an equivalent nuclear power programme. Moreover, the type and location of the jobs would be very different. Nuclear technology tends to create a few permanent technical jobs, together with a large number of temporary jobs in construction, often in remote areas. A programme of insulation and solar power development would, by contrast, create many jobs for building construction workers, plumbers and engineers in cities. Wind power development would create work for the aerospace industry, wave-power systems are well suited to development by shipbuilders; and the various new coal-based technologies (Combined Heat and Power and fluidised beds) would mean work for the power engineering industry.

An alternative 'renewable' energy and conservation technology programme would also require expansion in the production of basic construction materials: glass, aluminium, insulation and so on. Of course investment in nuclear power would also create jobs in the manufacturing and materials industries and, through the economic multiplier effect (when workers in these industries spend their wages, thus creating demand), jobs in the rest of industry. But the pattern of employment created would be different; as we have already said, the problem of structural unemployment could well be heightened by nuclear-power development.

In the absence of detailed analysis it is difficult to give an overview of the precise employment chains that the various options might create. But at the very least the alternative/conservation approach would create the *same* number of jobs, and arguably, a wider range of job types in a wider range of locations. The US Federal Energy Authority's *Project Independence* estimated that whereas nuclear energy production utilises two tradespeople to every professional

**Table 6**
Comparison of Job Intensities of Nuclear/Solar Resources in the USA

| Source | Energy ($10^{15}$ Btu's per year) | Cumulative person-years of labour (in millions) demanded to year 2000(a) |
|---|---|---|
| Heating and cooling(b) | 3.5 | 2.5 |
| Solar Thermal(c) | 1.3 | 1.0 |
| Windpower | 4.9 | 3.7 |
| Bioconversion(d) | 15 | 6.6 |
| Ocean Thermal | 7 | .9 |
| Photovoltaic(e) | 6.8 | 26.8 |
| **Total Solar** | $38.5 \times 10^{15}$ Btu's | $39 \times 10^6$ cumulative person years |
| **Total Nuclear** | $13 \times 10^{15}$ Btu's | $5.2 \times 10^6$ cumulative person years |

Source: Laitner, 'The Impact of Solar and Conservation Technologies upon Labor Demand', Conference on Energy Efficiency, Washington DC, May 1976. The data was extrapolated from the Solar Taskforce Report *Project Independence*, Federal Energy Authority, Washington DC, 1974.

(a) the total labour needed to develop the supply capacity by the year 2000.
(b) solar collectors used to feed conventional radiators or to provide heat for conventional absorption-type refrigerators
(c) producing electricity by raising steam
(d) fuel produced by organic processes
(e) solar cells

Comparing the totals for solar and nuclear it can be seen that to obtain $10^{15}$ Btu's of energy per year from solar sources would require $\frac{39.0 \times 10^6}{38.5}$ person-years, to obtain it from nuclear sources $\frac{5.2 \times 10^6}{13}$

person-years—that is approximately $1 \times 10^6$ and $.4 \times 10^6$ person-years respectively, or a ratio of 2.5 to 1.

**Table 7**
Financial Costs of Electric Technologies in the Year 2000

| Source | Capital to labour ($/person-year) | Energy to capital (Btu's/$) | Delivered cost to consumer ($ mills./KWh) |
|---|---|---|---|
| Nuclear | 79,721 | 31,540 | 35.6 |
| Solar Thermal | 56,538 | 22,413 | 25–30 |
| Wind | 33,784 | 39,200 | 13 |
| Ocean Thermal | 175,400[1] | 42,782 | 12.4 |
| Photovoltaic | 16,418 | 15,454 | 20–30 |

Source: as for Table 6 page 95.

1 Ocean thermal gradient energy conversion systems make use of the temperature differential between surface layers in the sea and water in the depths. They would have to be very large and very complex units, akin to oil rigs. Hence the very large capital to labour ratio.

scientist or technician, solar energy production uses nine to one—a much broader range of skills are necessary. And, as the next chapter illustrates, the development of alternative 'renewable' energy technologies and the more efficient use of our remaining fossil fuels, coupled with conservation measures, would not only create needed employment and make better social use of human skills and material resources: they could also, in fact, make it unnecessary to develop nuclear power.

## Alternative Employment Options—the Trade Union Response

The employment implications of the alternative energy options have not gone unnoticed by trade unionists. The current economic recession has led several groups of workers to campaign for product diversification as an alternative to redundancies, both in the power engineering industry and elsewhere.

A wide-ranging assessment of alternative energy options has been carried out by shop stewards at GEC, who have produced a report (*Workers' Power*) which, although giving cautious support to the AGR, leans heavily on non-nuclear energy developments—including wind and wave power. The Power Engineering Industry Trade Union Committee—which has representatives from GEC, Clarke Chapman, Babcock & Wilcox and C. & A. Parsons—is also actively investigating various alternative energy options. Although they have continued to back nuclear power—and large coal-fired plants—they have also called for a shift in emphasis to smaller conventional power plants which they argue 'are important because they are more labour-intensive than larger plants and cover the needs of the emerging nations'. They have also proposed increased research and development of renewable forms of energy, such as the utilisation of tidal, wind and wave power.

Shop stewards at the Gateshead plant of Clarke Chapman who manufacture large-scale boilers for power plants have taken these proposals a stage further and produced a 'Corporate Plan' outlining a wide range of alternative energy products: including solar, wind, wave and tidal systems, fluidised bed and Combined Heat and Power Units, and energy-storage systems which the workforce could produce, as an alternative to contraction in the industry.

This plan follows the approach pioneered by the Lucas Aerospace Combine Shop Stewards' Committee, who in 1976 produced a detailed 'Alternative Corporate Plan', drawn up as a radical and constructive alternative to redundancy in the aerospace industry. Similar proposals have emerged in other parts of the aerospace industry—at Rolls Royce, and at BAC Preston. The Lucas plan included proposals for products such as a heat-pump system for background heating in housing: two natural-gas-fuelled units are currently being tested in council housing. It also proposed switching circuits and pumping components for solar heating, and solar heating panels. There were also plans for investigating the application of advanced aerospace technology to wind power sources, and for developing power packs with low-pollution high-efficiency characteristics.

Similar proposals have been made by the Vickers National Combine Shop Stewards' Committee for diversification away from arms production at Barrow and Newcastle. Products proposed include wave power systems designed to use the existing shipbuilding expertise at Barrow. Support for this type of diversification programme has come from the TGWU and from AUEW (TASS) as well as from some sections of the Labour party.

The Yorkshire miners' leader, Arthur Scargill, through the 'Energy 2000' organisation (supported by Yorkshire and South Wales members of the National Union of Miners) has also been campaigning for the development of solar power and energy conservation measures, and appeared at the Windscale Enquiry arguing against the need to develop nuclear power.

There is an increasing feeling amongst some sections of the labour movement that energy policy is an important political issue, and that an energy strategy based on the development of alternative energy sources and conservation could provide adequate amounts of energy for a much smaller capital investment than nuclear power—thus freeing capital to be invested in other parts of the economy, such as the public services. In addition it is gradually being recognised that a bigger employment gain is possible through this strategy than through the adoption of nuclear power.

## US Trade Unions and Alternative Technology

Several major US trade unions have expressed considerable enthusiasm for the job-creating potential of solar power and related technologies. For example the President of the Sheet Metal Workers' International has commented: '. . . even figured conservatively, energy-saving modification work and an expanded use of solar energy could put all unemployed sheet metal workers back to work'.

While the President of the International Association of Machinist and Aerospace Workers has claimed:

'if, for example, the government launched a programme tomorrow morning to equip each home in America with a rooftop solar water heater, scores of factories would be retooled and re-opened. Thousands of jobs would be created for unemployed machinists and auto workers'.

In a report issued in February 1977, Frank Mills of the Sheet Metal and Air Conditioning Contractors Association in the US estimated that fitting 3 million homes for 60 per cent reliance on solar heating would create 12 million hours' work per year for 10 years (about 7000 jobs).

Another report estimated that the operation and maintenance of large wind power systems would require 19,000 more 'person years' work than an equivalent nuclear power programme.

Even the United Auto Workers of the US have supported solar power, together with other so-called alternative energy options as being likely sources of employment for the future.

### Alternative Industrial Strategy

The sort of political and economic strategy implied in the development of the alternative energy options is an important one for the labour movement. This strategy would emphasise investment in job-creating alternatives which meet real social needs. This does not necessarily imply opting for low productivity: rather, it is a matter of asking 'productivity for what social purpose and at what social cost?' Neither does it mean the abandonment of high technology: some mechanisation and automation measures do release workers from dangerous or boring occupations. Current trends are towards the replacement of almost all types of labour, particularly skilled labour, by advanced technology, and this means either redundancy or de-skilling. But this could be reversed: we could use technology to enhance skills rather than eliminate them—and at the same time decrease the length of the working week.[4]

What is being proposed is an industrial strategy which does not need an enormous increase in energy production, which could provide real long-term employment gains, and which would put a premium on meeting real social needs. What we are calling for is the adoption of labour-intensive energy conservation measures, and the development of alternative energy options coupled with support for new skill-intensive material recycling and equipment repair and renovation industries.[5] These developments, together with a new approach to food production and processing, improved building methods and public transport systems, could ensure continued employment and possibly a higher real standard of living for the majority, with less capital investment and little or no increase in energy production.

## Energy Growth and Standard of Living

It is widely held that there is a direct correlation between material standards of living and energy consumption. But although the heat supplied to our homes, which accounts for roughly a quarter of the UK's energy consumption, is 6 per cent more in 1978 than it was in 1950, the amount of heat supplied *per household* has *decreased*, the number of households having gone up by 2.5 million. And it is beyond question that the general standard of heating and comfort in most homes has increased and, as insulation standards and domestic technology improve, will rise further without increased energy consumption. So in the domestic sector there has been, and may well continue to be, an *inverse* correlation between energy consumption and standard of living.

Indeed, some energy analysts believe that we could actually *reduce* our energy consumption while *increasing* our standard of living. For example, Gerald Leach, Director of the Energy Project of the International Institute for Environment and Development, pointed out in his evidence to the Windscale Enquiry that given the introduction of fairly straightforward technical measures '. . . plausible projections can be made in which energy demand holds constant or even declines, while material standards improve'.

Gerald Leach has produced a low-energy scenario for the UK 1975–2025[6] which 'assumes considerable growth in material standards'. For example a 21 per cent increase in car ownership; a 32 per cent increase in average distance travelled per person annually; and a doubling of the number of domestic electrical appliances owned by householders by the year 2000, with proportionate increases by the year 2025. But according to his analysis '. . . despite substantial rises in material standards, mobility and other energy-related activities, energy demand falls considerably from present levels in all sectors over the next 50 years'. These reductions—of the order of 60 per cent in some cases—will be brought about, he feels, by the adoption of more rational technologies and techniques of energy production, conservation and use—for example better building design, insulation, the use of heat pumps, more efficient car engines (a 40 per cent saving by the year 2000), solar energy, and Combined Heat and Power systems.

So frugality is not a necessary part of an 'alternative' strategy. Neither are we arguing that we don't need growth. There are clearly many areas on which growth is vital; the social services, education, health care and so on, and there are many people who have yet to benefit from the fruits of affluence. We have a more or less no-growth economy for *some* people at present, and it is in no way a utopia.

Ardent conservationists tend to see 'growth' as the key problem. They argue that growth usually means the production and aggressive marketing of shoddy, planned obsolescent products which misuse scarce resources and do not meet social needs. Now this is clearly true. But the remedy is not just to halt growth. What we need rather is to fight for *selected growth* in socially needed production *and* for redistribution of economic power as a preliminary to moving, in a planned way, to a stable state economy in the longer term. Of course it may well be that, in the society of the future, growth will be reduced. It is difficult to predict changes in social values, priorities and perceptions of need. It could be that, at some stage, given a certain base-line of material affluence, people will be more concerned with 'quality of life' than with 'quantity of consumption'.[7] But whatever the longer-term possibilities, it is clear that a stable state economy can only be introduced as part of a democratically determined programme of political and economic changes—otherwise it will increase inequalities and exploitation.

So where do we go from here? What we are calling for is essentially an *alternative industrial strategy*—one that involves more than a few reforms. First, we are talking about social and economic planning; second, an assessment of the social, political and economic implications of technologies; third, the encouragement of workers' control and community control over industrial and commercial practices. As we have seen, workers at Lucas Aerospace, Vickers, Clarke Chapman and elsewhere are even now producing their own Corporate Plans for their respective companies. These plans place a premium on products which meet real social needs, that are not necessarily profitable in the conventional capitalist sense, but that do make economic sense in relation to mass unemployment and its economic and social costs.

The role of energy and energy technologies is basic to the preparation of a socialist political economy. We should aim to reverse the trend of displacement of labour by energy and capital; we should also be looking to the development of technologies which enhance the skills and control over the work-process of workers; and we should be assessing the outputs of industrial processes in the light of the necessity to increase the satisfaction of real social needs and decrease the wasteful production of such goods as armaments.

Clearly this implies some fairly drastic restructuring within the economy. Some industries would contract, but this could be done in a planned way, with provisions for retraining, so that workers would transfer to alternative equipment. Other industries would be able to convert or diversify to alternative production. If industrial conversion on this large scale seems utopian, remember that production in this country shifted rapidly from peacetime to wartime uses and back to peacetime uses in the period of the second world war.

It is also crucial for us to recognise the importance of having an industrial strategy which is part of the struggle for a socialist political economy. The struggle for control of technologies and the use of labour-power is an integral part of the struggle for socialism. In this process it is crucial for us to recognise the role of technology in the dominant capitalist ideology. If we accept that a future socialist economy is merely a change in ownership of capitalist-spawned productive apparatus, we are not honestly confronting the basic contradictions of the capitalist political economy.

In conclusion then, a rational and democratically planned socialist economy, which would abolish waste, planned obsolescence and overproduction, could, with the rational use of technology, provide real living standards in excess of what we 'enjoy' now. The decentralisation of the productive apparatus would enhance democratic control, and the reduction of capital inputs to industry would free resources for other social uses. This 'scenario' is already in the minds of some sectors of the labour movement: the time is ripe for these issues to receive widespread debate.

### References
1  See 'The Crisis Facing the UK Power Plant Manufacturing Industry', North East Trade Union Studies Information Unit November 1976.
2  For further discussion see 'The future isn't what it used to be', Nicholas Valery, *New Scientist* 13 January 1977; and 'Employment, Skills and Job Design in Engineering and Manufacturing', Centre for Alternative Industrial and Technological Systems 1978.
3  For further discussion see 'What Choice Windscale', C. Conroy, FoE/Consoc 1978.
4  See the Future of Work Course T262, Open University Press, 1975. In the interim the 35-hour week and earlier (phased) retirement are vital demands. Work sharing and a ban on overtime are equally important, although even harder to implement.
5  See for example the Batelle Memorial Institute study *The Potential for Substituting Manpower for Energy*, Social Affairs Division of the Commission of the European Communities, 1977.
6  Described in Gerald Leach's paper presented to the Economic Commission for Europe: United Nations Economic and Social Council, January/February 1978. The full IIED Scenario is to be published shortly.
7  Leach and others have pointed out that there are already signs of market saturation for some consumer items—a point made by the Energy Research Group in their 'Critique of the Electricity Supply Industry', ERG 013, Open University, 1976.

*Further reading:*
*Jobs From the Sun*, California Public Policy Centre 1978. This quotes a study by the California Employment Development Department which indicates that a solar programme would create 6.6 times more jobs per unit of energy produced than an equivalent nuclear programme, based on an assessment of the Sundesart nuclear plant project.

**Chapter 8** *Dave Elliott*

# Alternative energy options

The alternative energy field is a rapidly expanding one. Five years ago it was thought the preserve of well-meaning eccentrics and romantics. Now however the alternative 'renewable' sources—wind, sun, water power, biological wastes and organic materials—are beginning to attract the attention of energy planners and industrialists. It is worth noting the USA intends to obtain 24 per cent of its energy from solar and wind power by the year 2020—that is, 58 per cent of its current (huge) consumption.

But so far there have been few comprehensive analyses of the overall contributions that the 'natural' energy sources could make to meeting our needs in the UK—partly because of the lack of research funding. One exception is the report entitled *An Alternative Energy Strategy for the UK* produced by the National Centre for Alternative Technology (NCAT).

The following is a brief summary of the main features of an alternative energy scenario, based on a combination of renewable and non-renewable resources. This account is in no way comprehensive or detailed, but should at least indicate that, given sufficient funding, there is a viable alternative to nuclear power. A more detailed account can be found in the NCAT report and in Amory Lovins's book *Soft Energy Paths*, Penguin 1977. A detailed comparison of alternative energy scenarios is currently being made by the Department of Political Economy at the University of Aberdeen.

## A technical aside

Energy politics is complicated by the proliferation of technical terms, units and statistics, some of which obscure important value judgements.

As Peter Chapman points out in *Fuels Paradise* there is no shortage of 'energy'—for example, we receive more than enough for all conceivable purposes from the sun every day. The point is that, usually, we have to *convert* the energy contained in uranium, oil or coal in the ground or incoming solar, wind and tidal energy, into a form which we can use to do useful work—for example electricity to turn motors or run lights. It's the *end use* that is important to human beings. What we are facing at present is not an *energy gap* but a *technology gap*—we need to find efficient ways to convert energy into useful forms.

In this book we have frequently used 'tons of coal equivalent' (or millions of tons of coal equivalent, mtce) as a unit of comparison between energy systems. The idea is to calculate the amount of coal that would provide the same energy as the energy source under discussion. But this can be unflattering and unfair to some methods of energy conversion.

To understand this, we need first to make a distinction between *primary energy, delivered energy* and *useful energy.* Due to inefficiencies in energy conversion and distribution, something like 30 per cent of the primary input energy from coal, oil etc is wasted. The bulk of this loss is due to the basic thermodynamic inefficiency of the process of producing electricity by raising steam for turbogenerators— some 70 per cent of the energy content of the primary fuels is thrown away as waste heat.

But even when the 'delivered' energy finally arrives at the point of consumption, further losses of around 30 per cent occur in the appliances and processes in which it is used.

So overall, around 60 per cent of the energy contained in the primary fuels used in Britain is wasted in one way or another: only 40 per cent of it is actually 'useful' energy.

But not all energy conversion systems are so wasteful. Solar power units for example can produce useful energy without the thermodynamic limits and distribution losses discussed above.

So it is important to compare like with like. Rather than compare solar and coal using primary energy input, in terms of mtces or TWh (tera-watt hours) we should compare the *useful energy* consumed.

For example, statements are frequently made to the effect that solar energy can provide only 100 TWh annually and that this is only 4 per cent of the UK's primary energy need (2500 TWh). This comparison is unfair because it ignores that fact that the figures for the energy provided by solar panel systems are usually quoted in terms of *useful* energy (eg delivered heat), not in terms of primary solar input, and that in any case the conversion losses are much less with solar systems and the distribution losses are negligible. So the 100 TWh from solar should be compared with the UK's *useful* energy consumption—which is around 1000 TWh. Solar power could therefore, on this basis, provide 10 per cent of our energy needs.

**Renewable Sources**

Despite being starved of research funds, enthusiasts have already estimated that alternative technology using renewable sources of energy could make a significant contribution to our energy needs by the year 2020. For example:

*Wind power*: Mainly derived from offshore windmills storing energy as compressed air in the (by then) empty gas and oil wells, windpower could, on the evidence submitted by Dr Peter Musgrove at the Windscale Enquiry, provide 25 per cent of our electricity needs (equivalent to, say, 13 mtce). Current funding by the Department of Energy includes £75,000 for a design study of a large horizontal axis windmill, plus another £75,000 for a vertical axis machine. Total funding is currently about £1 million. The Electrical Research Association has estimated that Britain could generate 10 per cent of its electricity from wind for a capital cost of £1,500 million.

Windpower availability tends to coincide with peaks in energy demand (unlike solar energy). Sorensen in Denmark has shown that, given short-term energy storage, windpower systems would actually be more reliable than nuclear power plants in supplying energy continuously.

Until recently the biggest wind-powered generator ever built was the 1.25MW Smith-Putnam machine erected in 1941 on a wind-swept hill in central Vermont. In a 30 mph wind, its output could reach 1.5MW. An even bigger horizontal axis 2.0MW machine has now been set up in Tvind in Denmark, while Boeing is building a 2.5MW unit. Current thinking points to vertical axis machines located in offshore areas, but there would be a role for small (1KW) domestic units, particularly in rural areas.

*Solar power*: Mainly used for domestic space and water heating, using flat plate solar collectors; could, according to the UK section of the International Solar Energy Society, provide 14 per cent of our primary energy needs (equivalent to 35 mtce). At present DoE funding is £6 million. Photo-electric, solar-cell technology is currently developing rapidly and is likely to be a major energy supplier in the future, and direct solar pre-heating of water could have an immense role to play in the process industries.

*Wave power*: Wave power could, according to Dr Peter Chapman of the Open University's Energy Research Group, eventually provide up to 120 mtce which is one-third of our current total energy demand. A more conservative estimate from NCAT is 50 mtce by 2025—a figure supported by the Department of Energy's report 'Energy Research and Development in the UK' (1976). Total DoE funding is around £5.4 million at present. Dr Salter of Edinburgh University estimates that an investment of £1,000 million would allow us to generate sufficient electric power for the entire UK from waves.

Salter suggests chains of 'nodding ducks' off the coast of Scotland; they would absorb energy from the waves, converting it into electricity for transmission ashore by undersea cable. The pivoted units would each weigh 50,000 tons and would be linked to form chains perhaps 300 miles long. A one-tenth scale prototype is currently under construction. Obviously such proposals would have to be subject to careful environmental impact analysis.

Other sources include *tidal* and *geothermal* power (10 mtce); power from small hydro-electric generators in streams and rivers (5–10 mtce?); *methane* produced from organic waste (14 mtce); the production of fast-growing biomass energy crops and bisynthesis of fuels generally (14 mtce). Considerable energy savings (perhaps 50 mtce) could be made by widespread use of *heat pumps*—devices which operate like refrigerators running in reverse, pumping heat into the house. They are very efficient in energy terms; instead of using 1 kw of electricity to produce heat with an electric fire, by feeding the 1 kw to a heat pump you can get perhaps three times more heat output.

Taking these various contributions together we could have a total of 200 mtce or more. The NCAT's more cautious estimate for renewable sources is 1197 TWh—about half our present consumption—by the year 2025. A target of 100 mtce by the turn of the century from renewable sources would seem conservative. And then there may be contributions from completely new technologies and from integrated systems based on renewable sources. One possibility is to use windmill-generated electricity to electrolyse water—producing hydrogen gas. This can be stored as a gas, or as a liquid (cryogenically) or in solid form (as a metal hydride), and used when required either as a fuel direct, or via a fuel cell (a device which works like electrolysis in reverse) to produce electricity. It has been suggested that hydrogen could replace natural gas, electricity and oil as a basic fuel for many domestic and industrial purposes.

There is the whole area of *energy conservation*. The Building Research Establishment has estimated that 15 per cent of our

**Diagram 5:** Summary of alternative energy supply

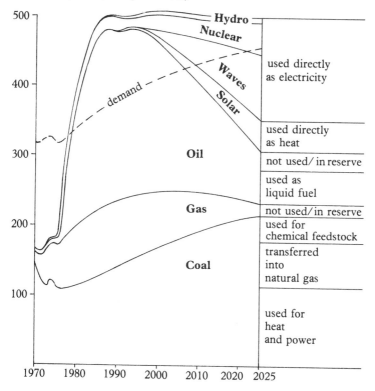

UK Primary fuel (mtce per annum)

Source: 'Alternative Energy Sources: an analysis of their role in energy policy.' Paper presented to the Royal Institution on Nuclear Power and the Energy Future, October 1977.

**Diagram 5:** Summary of a relatively conservative alternative energy scenario produced by Dr Peter Chapman of the Energy Research Group, Open University, which unlike the NCAT scenario (Diagram 6) includes a small contribution from nuclear sources in order to increase diversity and, one might add, to placate the nuclear industry.

However, Chapman notes that his energy supply policy '. . . maintains a surplus of energy production over the entire period. Also this policy has not pushed any energy source to its full capacity nor has it exhausted the scope for energy conservation.' It also ignores potential contributions from wind, solar, electric biomass and tidal sources.

primary energy could be saved by building insulation and improved design.

Leach, in his evidence to the Windscale Enquiry, suggested that in the short to medium term technical measures could reduce fuel consumption in road vehicles by 10–30 per cent and in the longer term by 40–50 per cent, while 20–40 per cent savings could be made in energy consumption in the energy-intensive industrial sectors. According to the evidence given by the Advisory Council of Energy Conservation to the Flowers Commission, a 20 per cent energy saving might be possible overall if a major energy conservation effort was made; while the Select Committee on Science and Technology suggest that a 15 per cent overall saving could be made without major changes ('Energy Conservation', September 1975).

### Non-Renewable Sources
But even so there could be a gap—at least until the renewable resources and conservation techniques were developed to their full potential, which could take several decades (as would, of course, the development of nuclear power).

At present our primary energy demand is around 340 mtce, and is expected by some authorities to rise to 500 mtce by the turn of the century—although, as noted earlier, such predictions are fraught with uncertainty. The Department of Energy have recently reduced their estimates by 20–30 per cent; while, as we have seen, Gerald Leach has suggested that demand might be cut even more dramatically.[1]

The shortfall could be met by our remaining fossil fuels—in the short term by oil and natural gas (150 mtce annually) and in the longer term coal. The NCB estimates that an annual output of 160 million tons could be maintained for 250 years, while Arthur Scargill's estimates are 250 million tons for 300 years. (It is worth noting that before the cutbacks in the coal industry in the 1960s Britain's mines were producing more than 200 million tons annually.)

If we were to rely on coal while the alternatives were developed, then: (1) Mining safety would have to be improved—by the adoption of automated remote control techniques, and, eventually, underground gasification and liquefaction of coal. (2) The efficiency of energy conversion and use should be increased, by the adoption of Combined Heat and Power (CHP) systems, linked to district heating network and a move away from the use of electricity for heating. It has been estimated that a full CHP programme would cost £3,000 million and take 25 years to complete. (3) Pollution controls should

**Diagram 6:** The NCAT alternative energy scenario based on the use of coal and renewable energy sources. Note that it proposes a gradual reduction, rather than increase, in our rate of *gross* energy consumption over the next 50 years, achieved largely by eliminating waste in energy conversion, distribution and use (chiefly through conservation and adoption of CHP and the use of heat pumps). However, net energy consumption by the year 2025 remains about the same as present: frugality is no part of this scenario. Indeed it anticipates 'increased comfort and levels of mobility for certain sectors of the community without demanding growth in useful energy consumption'.

SOURCES AND END USES OF ENERGY

SHOWING HOW THESE COULD CHANGE OVER 50 YEARS
WHILST INTRODUCING RENEWABLE SOURCES,
MAINTAINING CONSTANT END USE ENERGY
AND REDUCING WASTE

From: 'An Alternative Energy Strategy for the UK', NCAT 1978, 2nd edition

UNITS: Millions MWh/year or TWh/year

| | 2025 | 1975 | |
|---|---|---|---|
| | 200 | 440 | LOSS IN FUEL CONVERSION AND COMBUSTION |
| | | 290 | WASTE HEAT FROM ELECTRICITY GENERATION |
| Solar Energy | 200 | 540 | USEFUL LOW TEMPERATURE HEAT (<100°C) (SPACE HEATING, WATER HEATING, ETC.) |
| Coal/Synthetic Gas/Geothermal | 80 | | |
| Heat Extracted from Environment (HEAT PUMPS) | 160 | | HEAT |
| Wind and Wave Energy | 130 | 470 | USEFUL HIGH TEMPERATURE HEAT (>100°C) (INDUSTRIAL PROCESSES, COOKING, ETC.) |
| Coal Biofuels Synthesised Fuel | 340 | | |
| Heat Recovered from Elec. Gen. | 100 | | |

(THERMAL STORAGE)
(THERMAL STORAGE AT POINT OF USE)

| | 2025 | 1975 | |
|---|---|---|---|
| | 40 | 240 | WASTE HEAT FROM ELECTRICITY GENERATION |
| Firm Electricity Supply SEE p.23 | 90 | 90 | USEFUL ELECTRICITY FOR LIGHTING, ELECTRONICS, ETC. |

| | 2025 | 1975 | |
|---|---|---|---|
| Firm Electricity Supply SEE p.23 | 70 | 20 | ELECTRIC MOTORS |
| Synthetic Oil/Biofuels | 50 | 100 | ENGINES |
| | | 50 | WASTE HEAT FROM ENGINES |
| WASTE HEAT FROM ELECTRICITY GENERATION | 110 | | USEFUL MECHANICAL ENERGY (TRANSPORT, DOMESTIC, INDUSTRY) |
| WASTE HEAT FROM ENGINES | 170 | | LOSSES ASSOCIATED WITH MECHANICAL ENERGY PRODUCTION |
| FUEL CONVERSION LOSS | 40 | | |

ELECTRIC MOTORS
ENGINES
WASTE HEAT FROM ELEC. GEN.
WASTE HEAT FROM ENGINES
20
100
50
330

Coal Oil Gas Nuclear/Hydro-electric

Coal/Oil/Gas Nuclear/Hydro-electric

Coal
Oil
Gas
Nuclear
Hydro electric
(Electric Heating 110)

Energy Sources in 1975

Energy Sources in 2025

Nature of Energy Requirements at Point of Use and Associated Losses (zero growth in end use)

be improved. Fluidised bed coal combustion is one answer: municipal wastes can also be burnt using this technology. A demonstration plant is currently under construction in Britain at a cost of £17 million, by the National Coal Board in conjunction with the International Energy Agency.

In the long term we should seek gradually to reduce our reliance on coal, as the renewable sources were developed. Coal is too good to burn; it is a vital feedstock for our chemical industry. Until recently R & D on coal technology has been fairly small—£11 million— compared to the £120 million spent on nuclear power R & D annually. However priorities are changing. In May 1978 the government announced a £200 million coal R & D programme— including £50 million for the development of fluidised bed systems.

For comparison, at present our nuclear reactors together contribute some 12.7 mtce—that's less than 4 per cent of our total energy consumption. So, given the state of development of the two types of technology, which should we develop? Some people argue that since we have invested so much capital and expertise in nuclear technology we should continue with it. But the road ahead is likely to be even more difficult, dangerous and costly, whereas the technology for the alternative options is inherently less complex and could be developed rapidly and safely, although of course the environmental and social impacts of large schemes like tidal barrages should be carefully scrutinised.

The immediate need is for greater financial commitment to research into these various renewable and non-renewable alternatives. As already indicated, small projects, based in the main in universities, are already being funded by the Department of Energy. Several small firms and some larger companies are moving into the field. And as we have seen there is mounting pressure for product diversification from workers in firms facing falling demand for their traditional products.

Even so, there is a clear need for a rapid and more comprehensive and planned development of the alternatives—something that is unlikely while nuclear power dominates the energy planners' imagination and receives the bulk of the funding.[2]


## The Non-Nuclear Future

It is obviously impossible to provide a definitive analysis of the contributions which these various options could provide—in part because research on them has been starved of funds. The figures above are inevitably speculative. But it looks increasingly likely that, even on conservative estimates, the alternative sources could seriously challenge nuclear power.

For example, back in 1974, the CEGB research arm, CERL, concluded in a report entitled 'Potential of Natural Energy Sources' that 'if large amounts of energy storage were to become available, wind plant could be considered as competing with nuclear plant in supplying this stored energy'. If we move to a major nuclear programme, then, as Ryle has pointed out in *Nature* (1977), we will need large amounts of storage.

Official estimates of the contributions likely from alternative sources by the turn of the century are creeping up—from 2–3 mtce in toto a few years ago to 15 mtce each for solar and wave power in 1977 (Select Committee on Science and Technology), while a recent House of Commons paper (534-1) talked of a 10–20 mtce contribution from offshore windpower, and 25 mtce from wave-power.

Some people argue that at the present stage of their development the alternatives cannot really absorb large amounts of cash. To some extent this is a self-fulfilling prophecy. Only when money begins to flow into the alternatives will scientists and engineers in large numbers feel that it is worthwhile taking the professional risk of entering the field. It is a chicken-and-egg problem: until recently 'AT' has been the preserve of a few poorly-funded enthusiasts, and alternative technology is therefore still seen as somewhat marginal.

But, as indicated above, wind, wave, solar programmes could easily absorb £1000 million each over the next few decades. The research phase could be relatively short. For example Ryle[3] has estimated that after an 18-month R & D phase, costing some £1–2 million, production of 1MW windmills 'could build up over a five year period to 2000 units a year . . . divided approximately equally between the structural steel, the electrical and the aircraft industries'. He adds that by 1985 'wind energy could be providing more than 2.8TWh annually, and the energy consumed in the manufacture of each unit would be repaid in 6 to 12 months'.

By 1991 the wind system could '. . . be producing an annual output of 56TWh'. In which case of course it, and similar solar and wave programmes, would be competing for funds directly with the nuclear power programme—which, if it proceeds as envisaged by some nuclear enthusiasts, would begin to lift off in the mid-1980s in order to meet the supposed 100 mtce energy gap in the late 1990s and thereafter. (For further discussion see Amory Lovin's *Soft Energy Paths*, Penguin 1977.)

It might be argued that we should nevertheless continue with a *small* nuclear power programme 'just in case'. Certainly we have no option but to maintain and hopefully improve our existing nuclear waste treatment and storage system. And a policy of decommissioning existing nuclear power stations does seem somewhat extreme. But there would seem little point—particularly from a financial viewpoint—in pursuing a small conventional nuclear development programme. After all, because of the limited availability of uranium 235 fuel for conventional reactors it is the plutonium breeder or nothing in the long term; and this implies a major investment.

In this context it is worth noting that a fast breeder programme would take several decades to complete, and that although they eventually breed more fuel than they consume, the process takes many years. As Gerald Leach has put it: 'Fast breeder reactors can supply very little energy before the year 2000 yet by that date the UK must be well into a rapid and sustained transition away from oil and gas as fuels. CFR-1 (the proposed commercial-scale demonstration fast reactor) is therefore irrelevant to the major energy problem facing this country, while its high investment costs . . . could draw resources away from much more promising solutions'. (Gerald Leach in *Nuclear Crisis: a Question of Breeding*, ed. Montefiore and Gosling, Prism Press 1977.)

The opponents of nuclear power thus believe that the alternatives provide a *better* solution to our energy problems than nuclear power. They are not calling for a retreat to primitive medieval technologies and a frugal life-style. For them, far from being a symbol of progress, nuclear power represents an unfortunate technological cul-de-sac while, in Leach's words, the development of the alternatives represents 'one of the most exciting—and as yet under-explored and under-financed—technological challenges of our time'.

## Fusion

A possible 'high' technology alternative that has yet to be mentioned is nuclear *fusion*. Fusion reactions between light elements, like hydrogen and its isotopes, occur in the sun and in hydrogen bombs and are the source of enormous amounts of energy. So far scientists have been unable to sustain a controlled fusion reaction for long enough, or at high enough temperatures and energy densities, for fusion to be a credible energy source. But it could be that, in a few decades or so, the fusion option will be viable. Research is proceeding along two lines: magnetic containment of hot plasmas in torroidal reactors like the Soviet Tokomak and the European JET at Culham;

and the use of lasers to produce high temperatures and densities in solids.

Assuming that some viable system is devised, there will then be very difficult technological problems in extracting useful energy. Direct conversion of 'hot' ions into electricity through magneto hydro dynamic (MHD) systems is one as-yet-untried option: otherwise we are back to trying to raise steam from a heat source operating at say 100 million degrees centigrade.

The most likely approach is to try to absorb the high energy neutrons produced by fusion reactions using a lithium blanket acting as a heat exchanger. The technological problems have yet to be fully considered, much less resolved—for example intense neutron bombardment may have significant effects on the surrounding materials and equipment, which may therefore have to be replaced regularly. All in all, it seems likely that the costs of fusion systems will be enormous and may preclude viable economic operation. And although the basic fuel is abundant—most of it can be obtained from sea water—lithium reserves are very limited.

There might be fewer problems of active waste disposal than with fission reactors, although the operational safety problems might well be serious—highly radioactive tritium is a byproduct of the fusion reaction.

Obviously this is an option that will—and should—continue to attract attention, even though it seems unlikely to be available in time to solve any of the energy problems that may emerge over the next few decades. Indeed, by the time it is ready (if it ever is), we shall presumably have had to resolve these problems in other ways.

It is also worth pointing out that research and development work on *fission* contributes only marginally to solving the problems of *fusion*: they are completely different processes. So if fusion were successfully developed, fission would be outflanked and seen as a technological dead end.

Finally it should be pointed out that there are, in any case, ultimate limits to how much energy we can release on this planet without significantly damaging the eco-system. Thermal pollution is already a problem in some areas, adversely affecting local climates. Fusion power, like coal, oil and fission (all of which involve releasing energy locked up in chemical or nuclear form) would simply help us to reach the final 'thermal barrier' faster.[4] In the long term the only solution is to opt for the natural renewable energy sources—solar, wind, wave, tidal.

These involve redistributing and using incoming solar radiation and gravitational forces from the sun and the moon: the net balance remains the same. Even so, we would have to take care to avoid local climatological effects, which is one reason why many alternative technologists feel that 'AT' should be used decentrally. Most of the renewable resources—solar, wind, etc.—are naturally distributed: it is, they argue, foolish to try to concentrate them in giant solar collector arrays or windmill parks so as to continue to feed grid systems. Enthusiasts for decentralisation are also perturbed by the prospect of giant wave-power units feeding the grid. While they see a role for some centralised units, and for the grid as an energy distribution medium, they would prefer the emphasis to be on smaller, community-scaled technology since, in theory at least, this would be more easily subject to democratic control.[5]

## The Politics of Alternative Technology

We have stressed in this book that nuclear technology reflects the society which generated it. The same is obviously true of 'alternative' technology. It follows therefore that it will not be sufficient *simply* to develop and implement alternative technologies: political and economic changes must also be made and should be reflected in the *type* of alternatives chosen. This is not the place to explore this issue further—it has been the subject of several recent books.[6]

But it should be clear that the above proposals would only make sense in a society in which exploitation of producer and consumer, planned obsolescence, spurious consumerism and all the other outgrowths of capitalism were abolished. Because the alternative technologies are mainly, by their nature, decentralised they can support a decentralised society, based on community and workers' control. But their introduction into society *as it is* clearly doesn't necessarily guarantee that such a state of affairs will come about.

The large monopolies will no doubt (and are trying to) co-opt alternative technology. There's money to be made—whether in the development of giant solar schemes or in selling (or renting) small planned-obsolescent solar units to private householders (already a £1 million market in the UK). Which is why it is vital that organised labour ensures that if we do make a transition to alternative technology, it is done in a way that at the very least does not reinforce the control of the monopolies and lead to further inequalities in society. The fight for alternative technologies is not an alternative to the fight for socialism. It can and should be part of it.

## References

1  See IIED [International Institute for Economic Development] report 'Low Energy Scenario for the UK 1975–2025', 1978.
2  Just how such a programme should be implemented and co-ordinated in institutional terms is currently under intense discussion. Many enthusiasts for 'decentral' technology would find the creation of a new centralised government agency to oversee the development of alternative technology an anathema, and they would be suspicious of locating alternative technology research in institutions like the various UKAEA research establishments which have historically been geared to nuclear technology.
3  Martin Ryle, 'Economics of Alternative Energy Sources', *Nature*, Vol. 267, 12 May 1977.
4  For further discussion see P. Chapman, *Fuel's Paradise*, Penguin 1976.
5  For further discussion see 'Community Technology', G. Boyle, Course T-361 Open University Press 1978, and 'Radical Technology', P. Harper & G. Boyle, Wildwood 1976.
6  For example, see David Dickson, *Alternative Technology and the Politics of Technical Change*, Fontana 1973.

**Part 3**

# Political strategies

So far the opponents of nuclear power have been mainly 'concerned' middle-class environmentalists, together with a sprinkling of radicals. The first part of this section outlines the strategies they have adopted and indicates some of the problems raised by what is to some extent a 'single issue' campaign.

The second part provides a brief checklist of questions and issues which may be of practical use to trade unionists.

The key message of the final chapter is that, although it is obviously important to build a broadly based anti-nuclear movement, opposition to nuclear power will never be effective unless it takes account of trade-union problems and concerns. The anti-nuclear movement must thus be ready to take up issues of immediate relevance to workers, such as occupational health and safety, employment and trade-union rights; and at the same time widen the range of debate and, in particular, demonstrate that there are viable, safer and more desirable alternatives.

**Chapter 9** *Dave Elliott*

# The anti-nuclear movement

## The Growth of the Anti-Nuclear Movement

Opposition to civil nuclear power has grown in most advanced industrial countries over the past decade. Some of the underlying environmental social and political reasons for this have been discussed in previous chapters. In this final chapter I want first to review the activities of the various anti-nuclear movements world-wide, and move on from descriptions to a discussion of strategy.

Some of the earliest cases of opposition occurred in the USA—for example in 1956 against the Enrico Fermi plant in Detroit (which later suffered a major accident). Construction at a number of plants was halted following citizen opposition through the courts in the early 1960s—for example at Bodega Bay and Malibu in California and at Ravenswood, New York. A much larger wave of opposition began in the late 1960s and has yet to abate—mainly as a consequence of the US environmental movement.

Some hundred or more legal interventions have been made by citizens through the courts in the USA, although in the majority of cases the effect has been to delay rather than stop construction.

Intervenors have grown in strength and technical ability, but since the mid-1970s many activists have come to believe that legal intervention alone will not divert the US government from its nuclear path. Consequently many have turned to non-violent direct action, demonstrations and citizen occupations of proposed reactor sites. This move to direct action occurred even earlier in continental Europe, where public consultation has been replaced—or at least augmented—by public confrontation.

The widely publicised violent confrontations with riot police in Germany and France in recent years have been used to portray the anti-nuclear movement as made up of anarchistic 'chaotics'. Although there are certainly libertarian—and communistic—tendencies in the movement, the bulk of it is made up of ostensibly apolitical environmentalists, concerned residents and, in some locations, farmers or fishermen, together with a core of anti-technocratic student activists whose politics vary from liberal to extreme left.

The following is a list of some of the major confrontations that have occurred in continental Europe in recent years.

### *Wyhl, West Germany, February 1975*
18 February: Several hundred protestors occupied the proposed site of a reactor as bulldozers moved in to start work, but were forced to retreat on 20 February, when a thousand riot police turned water cannons on them. The police then built a barbed wire fence around the site.

The next day 5000 people demonstrated against this action and on 23 February a major demonstration ensued, involving some 28,000 people. Despite the presence of 3000 police the demonstrators recaptured the site, tore down the fences and set up a permanent encampment which operated as a 'free university' for nine months, until the German courts imposed a ban on construction, pending further research on environmental impact. A similar non-violent occupation occurred at nearby *Kaiseraugst* in Switzerland in April 1975, involving 16,000 people. The site remained occupied for five months. In March 1977 a court ruled that the Whyl Plant should be condemned on safety grounds.

### *Brokdorf, West Germany, November 1976*
13 November: 30,000 people attended what was to be a peaceful demonstration near the site of a new reactor on the River Elbe.

Some 3000 demonstrators tried to occupy the site and there were violent clashes with the police, who used water cannons, tear-gas grenades and baton charges, and even resorted to attacks with low-flying helicopters.

A similar battle took place in March 1977 at *Grohnde*, near Hamelin, where 10,000 demonstrators were met with armoured vehicles, tear gas and water cannons. There have been follow-up demonstrations at Brokdorf.

### *Malville, France, July 1977*
60,000 demonstrators from many countries attempted to march on the site of France's first commercial fast breeder reactor—and were met with a massive police attack, in which one demonstrator was killed and several police seriously injured (some by prematurely exploding percussion grenades). Attacks and arrests continued into the night as demonstrators were hounded from the scene.

### *Kalkar, West Germany, 25 September 1977*
60,000 people attempted to march on the site of a proposed 300MW prototype fast breeder reactor. 7500 police surrounded the site, 2000

occupied the site itself while 4000 waited in reserve. Police harassment of people arriving for the demonstration significantly reduced its effect, and no attempt was made to occupy the site—not surprisingly, given the four-foot-deep water-filled moat and ten-foot-high concrete wall that had been built to protect it. There were no incidents—although 150 people were arrested before the march started.

## Spain, September 1977
600,000 people took part on a protest at the pressurised water reactor being built by Westinghouse at Lemoniz. Another demonstration at Zaragoza mobilised 100,000.

## Bombings in France
The 'terrorist' image of the anti-nuclear movement has been re-inforced by a series of bomb attacks on installations in France. For example on 4 May 1975 at the Fressenheim plant (itself a target for an earlier major demonstration) the reactor core casing was 'slightly' damaged by a bomb. On 6 June 1975 the Paris offices and factories of Framatome, a subsidiary of US Westinghouse were bombed: at Argenteuil, a workshop testing valves for reactors was damaged, while at Courbevoie the input terminals of Framatome's main computer were destroyed.

On 15 August two further bombs damaged part of a turbine and communications equipment at a power station at Monts d'Arée—allegedly the work of Breton separatists. Similar incidents in *Spain* have been the work of Basque separatists. On 19 December 1977 a four-man ETA commando team tried to storm the guard post outside the Lemoniz site, unsuccessfully. On 17 March 1978 a bomb went off inside the plant, killing two workers.

## Non-violent actions in the USA
Far less press coverage has been given to the series of non-violent citizen occupations of nuclear sites that have occurred in the USA.

A series of demonstrations have taken place at Seabrook, New Hampshire, culminating in a non-violent citizens occupation by the Clamshell Alliance in May 1977, involving some 2000 people, 1400 of whom were arrested and incarcerated by the National Guard for two weeks—an event which generated considerable public debate and some sympathy for the anti-nuclear cause.

The Clamshell Alliance took great pains to avoid confrontation. They insisted that everyone attending the demonstration undergo several hours training in the techniques of non-violence, including role-playing exercises to avoid confrontation psychology. These proved invaluable both during the occupation and during the two weeks of imprisonment.

Similar actions have occurred throughout the USA. In July 1977, 700 members of the Crabshell Alliance staged a peaceful demonstration at Elma, Washington, while 50 members of the Abalone Alliance were arrested after peacefully occupying the site of a reactor at San Luis Obispo, California. Eighty members of the Trojan Decommissioning Alliance were arrested after demonstrating against the Trojan reactor in Rainer, Oregon.

In June 1978, a second major citizens' rally was organised by the Clamshell Alliance at Seabrook, and there are plans to mount a 'non-violent blockade' to stop the arrival by sea of the reactor vessel.

So far there has been no violence at any US anti-nuclear demonstration, and as a result public opinion is somewhat more favourably disposed to the anti-nuclear movement.

However in Australia police have cracked down heavily on a number of dockside demonstrations against the shipment of uranium by Australian anti-nuclear activists—despite the fact that some trade unions had until recently been imposing a ban on the transport and mining of uranium. In Sweden and Denmark, public expression of concern over nuclear power has had a major impact on government policy. Indeed, in Sweden the pro-nuclear stance of the Social Democratic government was one element in their election defeat in 1976—although there is little evidence so far that the incoming centre-right party will in practice be willing to halt Sweden's ambitious nuclear programme.

Public opposition in Holland has been somewhat more effective; it resulted in 1974 on a government moratorium on new reactors. The German anti-nuclear movement has also been relatively successful. Court orders and administrative decisions following the widespread citizen actions described earlier have slowed down the government's nuclear programme—although they have not halted it.

### The anti-nuclear movement in Britain

In Britain so far the situation is, to say the least, quieter. Most opposition has taken the form of legal intervention, petitions and lobbying—much as in the USA and Europe up to a few years ago. But little has been visible to oppose: until the recent decision to build two new AGRs, no new plants had been proposed (the existing AGR programme dates from 1965). The major focus of concern has been the Windscale reprocessing plant.

In April 1976, the Friends of the Earth organised a 'nuclear excursion' by train for some 600 people to Windscale to protest against the expansion plans. Smaller demonstrations were also held at Torness and Sizewell. In November 1976 CANTO (an alliance of anti-nuclear activists) organised a demonstration in Trafalgar Square, which received considerable press coverage despite being poorly attended. In February 1977 several hundred inhabitants of the Orkney Islands protested against the prospect of uranium mining. A similar protest involving 3500 people occurred in Galloway, following suggestions that nuclear waste might be dumped there. 600 members of Energy 2000, a coalition of trade unionists and environmentalists, lobbied parliament in November 1977. Greenpeace (London) have organised a number of protests against uranium shipments, and against the VRENCO contract.

Finally, Friends of the Earth organised a major London demonstration against the Windscale expansion on 19 April 1978, which attracted 12,000 people. In May 1978 SCRAM (the Scottish Campaign to Resist the Atomic Menace) mounted the first large-scale rally, attended by 4000 people, at the proposed site of an AGR at Torness.

Most of the anti-nuclear groups (FoE, Consoc, SERA, etc) submitted evidence to the Windscale Enquiry. In fact the Windscale Enquiry looks like being a watershed in the development of the British anti-nuclear movement. Until the publication of Mr Justice Parker's report in March 1977, most activists felt, at least publicly, that there was some virtue in opposing nuclear power through official channels by presenting detailed evidence to planning enquiries. Friends of the Earth, for example, have suggested that such activities provide public airing of the issues, whatever the actual outcome.

But involvement in public enquiries and detailed technological debate is time- and money-consuming for voluntary environmentalist groups. Many anti-nuclear groups have therefore begun to doubt the wisdom of further involvement—for example, with the proposed enquiry on the fast breeder reactor—since this could tie up resources which could otherwise be used in organising a wider anti-nuclear movement.

The failure of the anti-nuclear movement to make any impact on the outcome of the Windscale Enquiry and, more particularly, the dismissive tone of the Parker Report, has strengthened the case for abandoning further involvement in official 'consultation' exercises.

As Jeremy Bugler put it in the *New Statesman* of 10 March 1978: '. . . until now the anti-nuclear forces in Britain have shown themselves willing to protest "within the system". In sharp contrast to French or German opponents they have argued that society can be persuaded from nuclear power. But Parker does not offer dialogue . . . it will not be surprising if the anti-nuclear movement here now changes its approach.'

What alternative approaches are likely to be adopted? One option is to hold a rival 'fringe' peoples' enquiry parallel with official enquiries like that on the FBR, with a major emphasis on viable alternative energy options; but this could easily be ignored or portrayed as irrelevant by the media. A more dramatic option is direct action through non-violent civil disobedience, for example occupation of reactor sites along the lines pioneered at Wyhl and Seabrook.

But even if official reports were widely perceived as being discredited or biased and the existing democratic process was felt to have been exhausted, it is doubtful whether this tactic—which in the extreme involves impeding construction work—would ever gain widespread public support: particularly, given the opportunities for confrontation between workers and protestors. That is not to say it won't be tried. SCRAM have already mounted a 'dry run' at Torness, and indicated that if construction started, they would be back in force.

But so far, the 'citizens' occupation' tactic as adopted in the US and Europe has really been used only as an extension of conventional protest. Although the threat of halting construction work has been there, in practice the political aim of groups like the Clamshell Alliance seems to have been to use occupation and the fact that large numbers of people were willing to be arrested, to embarrass officials and put pressure on decision makers to reverse official policy. Whether this sort of approach will be any more effective than conventional lobbying, legal intervention and demonstrations is an open question. It may be that despite all attempts to avoid violence, given unyielding officials, if this tactic was pursued on a large scale, confrontation would be inevitable.

In Britain what is more likely is a gradual increase in conventional public demonstrations of opposition to nuclear power, without confrontation. Certainly there are increasing numbers of people in Britain who are uncertain about nuclear power, and who might lend support to an opposition campaign along CND lines—and of course this could 'tip-over' into direct action at some stage. There are already signs of militant opposition from people faced with the prospect of uranium mining or nuclear waste dumping in their locality.

However, it seems unlikely that a really large or militant anti-nuclear movement will develop in the UK until people are faced with actual proposals for reactors on their doorsteps. If a large-scale nuclear programme is pursued (remembering that the UKAEA would like to have 30GW of installed nuclear capacity by 1990—that is an equivalent to 25 reactors), then large numbers of people might become concerned. And it would not be just local residents. Many others might be exposed to risks as a consequence of increased transport of fuel and waste round the country between power stations and reprocessing plants.

## Some Results of a *New Society* Survey on Attitudes to Nuclear Power (1977)

'In general, do you favour or oppose the building of more nuclear power stations in Britain to produce electricity?'

Favour 49%
Oppose 32%
Don't know 19%
No. in sample: 1081.
'Eventually, coal, oil, and natural gas will run out. Which of these two do you think is the best way of tackling this problem?'

| | |
|---|---|
| Start building more nuclear power stations now, to ensure future supplies of energy | 32% |
| Do everything possible to save coal, oil and gas and continue looking for other sources of energy apart from nuclear power | 61% |
| Don't know | 7% |

Source: *New Society* 31 March 1977

### The Ideology of the Anti-Nuclear Movement

Whatever happens in the UK, it seems clear that the anti-nuclear movement worldwide will continue to grow, unless nuclear power is abandoned by the various national governments. Already in Germany, France, Holland, Denmark, Sweden, Spain, the USA and Australia, nuclear power is a central political mobilisation issue.

In the USA the anti-nuclear-power movement has grown out of

125

the environmental movement, but it has also attracted many of the radicals and pacifists who were active in the civil rights and anti-war movements. In Germany and France there is some representation from both the marxist left and the anarchist movement, although the bulk of the support comes from environmentalists, local residents and farmers—many of them conservative. Indeed, in Germany the fear of being branded 'communist' has led the anti-nuclear citizen groups—who draw much of their support from local winegrowers, housewives and the clergy—to try to exclude 'extremists'. For example, a demonstration was mounted in November 1975 at Wippingen by 1500 entirely local people, who tried to indicate their origins and ward off any hint of 'communist' involvement by fielding 800 tractors. Obviously these movements have also attracted students, but it is clear that, despite allegations otherwise by government spokesmen, the citizens' movement is far from being communist-inspired and -organised. But that is not to say it is not potentially a radical movement.

The starting point for citizen opposition to nuclear power has in many cases been concern by local farmers, winegrowers and fishermen for their livelihood, coupled with the residents' fear of radioactive pollution. This tends to become generalised into a wider resentment against centralised government arrogance and steam-roller decision-making.

As Peter Taylor has commented in *The Struggle Against Nuclear Power in Central Europe*:

'A political movement is underway, at present only diffuse, but a definite philosophy is emerging from an initially unstructured resentment and opposition to centralised State Plans that impose upon the individuals rights, be they so simple as the right to say . . . "no" . . . and be taken heed of, or as complex as the right to an unpolluted environment'. (*The Ecologist* Vol. 7 No. 6, July 1977)

What is emerging is a populist resentment against 'big government' and a general distrust of technocrats, which transcends the specific issues of nuclear power and environmental pollution.

As Nelkin has put it:

'. . . contemporary resistance to technological change is often marked by hostility to public bureaucracies and resentment of impersonal expertise-dominated policies. The issue is no longer simply the social or environmental impact of science and technology, but the locus of power and control over major public decisions.' (D. Nelkin, *The Politics of Participation*, Sage Publications 1977).

At the very least it seems clear that citizens who might accept an adverse decision which was made in a way perceived to be democratic, will resist decisions made by technocrats without any real consultation.

Some parts of the anti-nuclear movement have specifically chosen to appeal to social-democratic values. As the European journal *Agenor* has put it, talking of the French and German experience:

'The nuclear option was taken without an adequate process of information and democratic debate. Individual decisions about reactors are imposed in a way that makes a mockery of the formal rights of citizens to object. Far from "undermining" the democratic system the citizen action movements are trying to win a democratic say in what directly affects them. It is governments which use police violence to force through their programmes, against widespread opposition (even over-riding legal judgements), and who are putting the democratic system at risk.' (*Agenor* 65, May 1977.)

In the USA the point has long since passed where anti-nuclear activists believed that the legal procedures were fair; but until recently that was still the position in the UK—despite the fact that the provisions for citizens' involvement in regard to nuclear policy are far less generous than in the USA. However, as we have already noted, the outcome of the Windscale Enquiry might change this. Although the public enquiry itself had all the trappings of a 'full and frank' exploration of the issues, in this report the inspector came down heavily in favour of expanding the reprocessing facilities, and his report conveyed very little of the complex arguments against the proposals presented at the Enquiry. Many people reacted to it as both superficial and biased.

As Ian Breach commented in *New Scientist*, the people most offended by Parker's report were 'those who were under no illusions . . . about the possible outcome, but who were expecting a report that would, as near as realistically possible, reflect the detail and the character of their case'.

Even so, it will be for only a minority of people that the public participation procedures and the existing democratic processes have been discredited. The majority will no doubt continue to believe in the effectiveness of Royal Commissions, Select Committees and public enquiries. It is usually only those people who have a particular interest to defend—local residents, or groups with some general policy objection—who, having tried to operate through the 'official' channels, begin to suspect their impartiality and legitimacy. Of course their experience can be generalised through the media, so that others begin to have doubts about the process. And at some point there will be public pressure for reforms of the decision-making process.

But this takes time, and can divert resources and energy from tackling the substantive *policy* issue. That's one reason why some anti-nuclear groups feel that involvement in the formal procedures is not only irrelevant but can be counterproductive. On the other hand, some political activists argue that it is equally vital to expose the bias of the decision-making and 'participation' procedures and show the political and economic forces at work. It is, they say, difficult to win support for direct action until official procedures have been discredited.

Whichever tactic predominates, there remains the crucial strategic question of the political effectiveness of 'single issue' campaigns. The anti-nuclear movement encompasses a wide range of groups, unified mainly through their concern with nuclear power, but diverging on many other issues.

A specific danger of the single-issue approach is that the existence or development of 'nuclear power plants' themselves begins to be seen as *the* problem. Horror stories about melt-downs and radioactivity produce a state of terror which can easily become irrational. 'Nukes' take on a semi-mythical role as symbols of evil, a tendency reinforced by the tactical requirements of mass opposition movements.

Now although an emotional response to a dangerous or socially undesirable technology is not necessarily a bad thing, uncritical fervour and blind fear can be profoundly reactionary. Belief that nukes are evil, bad and dangerous can be manipulated to provide support for reactionary policies. This can be avoided only if people can see beyond the specific technology to the forces which create it—that is, if they can develop a rational political analysis in which to locate nuclear power.

## Environmentalism—Ideology and Practice

Despite protestations otherwise, the environmental movement, of which the bulk of the existing anti-nuclear movement in Britain and elsewhere is part, is a political movement. Many environmentalists seek major changes in society—for example decentralisation, less emphasis on materialism and on economic growth. Some of their blueprints for the future have much in common with anarcho-syndicalist utopias—although there are crucial differences, particularly in the means felt appropriate for attaining the utopian end.

Some of the more conservative groups see change coming through reforms orchestrated by government, while other more anarchistic-minded groups hope for spontaneous developments at the grass roots. Some groups, like the Ecology Party, profess not to subscribe to the idea of a 'parliamentary road' to ecological utopia but have fielded candidates at elections.

Nevertheless, environmentalism is projected as being an 'apolitical' moral or ethical position supported by ecological analysis. This is not the place to explore all the implications (it has been done efficiently elsewhere, for example in Hans Magnus Enzensberger's 'Critique of Political Ecology' in *Raids and Reconstructions: Essays in Politics, Crime and Culture*, Pluto Press 1976) but it is clear that there are within the environmental movement many political stands, some progressive and some reactionary.

Symbolic rejection of materialism by the affluent jostles with economic protectionism. Romantic utopianism is coupled with thinly disguised elitism. Libertarian sentiments compete with a belief in the need to reimpose 'natural order'. While the Ecology Party in its 1974 Manifesto proposed a major social restructuring, the decentralisation of industry and of political control. it made no mention of redistribution of wealth or earning power—indeed, it called for continued wage restraint and a statutory wages policy.

But the Conservative and right-wing tendencies in the environmental movement are more than offset by the preponderance of radicals, drawn together by their common disaffection with the existing order. At the grass roots level, environmental groups are often allied with self-help and community-action projects—and are beginning to forge links with the trade union and labour movement. The Green Ban Action Committee in Birmingham is a good example. (See 'Trade Unions, Technology and the Environment'. Course T-361, unit 9, Open University Press 1978.)

The mobilisation of the various stands within the environmental movement on the issue of nuclear power will no doubt heighten many of the contradictions and splits—and, hopefully, clarify its politics.

## The Left on Nuclear Power

Although some radical groups have developed general analytic positions on nuclear power, their main contribution in general has been to present criticisms of the tactics adopted by the anti-nuclear movement, focusing in particular on the anti-nuclear movement's policy of 'non-confrontation' and 'non-violence'.

The Canadian anarchist paper *Open Road* alleges that in Europe the leadership of the various environmental groups 'has actively suppressed all organic discussion of any tactic other than non-violence and civil disobedience, even to the point of exposing thousands of unprepared people to violent attacks by the police and military'. (*Open Road*, Fall 1977)

The same cannot be said of the Clamshell Alliance, who at least ensured everyone involved was trained to avoid violence, and provided effective organisation and communications during the demonstrations. But even so, some US critics resent the domination of the movement by pacifist liberals and Quakers.

The other major criticism, made for example in the US radical magazine *Science for the People*, is that the emphasis is too much on large symbolic demonstrations attended by 'weekend warriors', whereas what is needed is painstaking organisation in the community and the creation of links with labour. (*Science for the People* July–August 1977)

Policy on nuclear power varies amongst the marxist groupings. The Socialist Workers' Party has come out firmly against nuclear power—supporting FoE's anti-Windscale demonstration and devoting considerable space in *Socialist Worker* to the nuclear issue. This followed a flurry of critical letters from readers in response to two articles by Duncan Hallas which argued that 'technology is neutral' and that 'nuclear power, as such, is of immense potential benefit to humanity, provided safety is put first' (4 December 1976).

The International Marxist Group have also come out against nuclear power, while *Socialist Challenge* has carried regular articles from anti-nuclear activists. The *Big Flame* group also has initiated a debate on nuclear power.

The Workers' Revolutionary Party is firmly against nuclear power under capitalism and its daily, *Newsline*, has carried a number of very informative articles on the issues. Their special pamphlet 'The Windscale Threat' elaborates on their political analysis as follows:

'The drive towards building more nuclear power stations and reprocessing centres at this time under capitalism, does not represent any development of productive forces. On the contrary capitalism in its worldwide crisis inevitably turns the conquests of science and technology into forces of destruction.'

But it also comments:

'This destruction is not the consequence of atom fission itself. The knowledge was used in this way because of the requirements of the ruling class. Only the socialist revolution can create the society based on planned production for human need which can utilise this knowledge for the development of mankind.'

The Workers' Socialist League and *Socialist Press* have come out against Windscale, but argue that political control over the development of nuclear power is the key issue. They have called for, amongst other things: 'No further work on reprocessing, FBR and other reactors until safety precautions are acceptable to workers' committees whose members must be drawn from *all* industries' and for 'an increase in state spending on all aspects of research into the exploitation of nuclear power under the control of elected workers' committees.'

'Although the Communist Party traditionally is in favour of 'technological advance', seeing it as socially progressive, it is aware that nuclear power could present problems. As the *British Road to Socialism* puts it: 'Further large-scale nuclear development should only take place if and when the vital issues of safety and our responsibility for the future of humanity are satisfactorily resolved.' (Fifth ed. 1978.) The *Morning Star* ran a series of pro- and con-articles in spring 1977, while the Young Communist League paper *Challenge* has a definite anti-nuclear bias. The CP's Science and Technology Sub-Committee has recently produced a discussion document, 'Long term strategy for energy policy', which poses 'nuclear' and 'non-nuclear' options without recommending either.

In general, while many left groups are currently critical of nuclear power as developed by capitalism, there still remains a belief, at least amongst some of the more traditional marxists, that nuclear power could be beneficial under socialism.

## Nuclear Power in the Communist Bloc

'Although nuclear power is dangerous within a capitalist economy, its development under socialism would be less hazardous because the technology would be geared to health, safety and welfare and not motivated by the dictates of profit.'

Arguments like this one—from the US left journal *The Guardian*—have been used to explain or justify the nuclear power programmes in the USSR, Cuba and China.

But would nuclear power be any safer under socialism? The first point is, of course, that it depends what you mean by socialism. We can only speculate on what might be perceived as necessary in a fully democratised self-managed society, but it does seem unlikely that nuclear power would be needed—or tolerated. But the technocratic leadership of state-capitalist countries like the USSR clearly considers nuclear power to be vital. The public has had little opportunity to influence their decisions.

And as Alan Roberts has commented: '. . . the absence of genuine public discussion on the issues involved in nuclear power has allowed the Soviet nuclear industry to "solve" its [waste] disposal problems with a breathtaking lightmindedness: high level radioactive wastes are simply pumped under pressure into deep permeable zones. Thus they are irretrievable; in insecure liquid form; and moreover (because of the high pressure of injection) a threat to the stability of the whole region; disposal methods with these objectionable features would never be permitted in the USA or Europe.' (*The Hazards of Nuclear Power*, Spokesman, 1977.)

It seems likely that the major nuclear accident that occurred in the Southern Urals in 1958 was related to underground waste storage. According to Zhores Medvedev (*The Hazards of Nuclear Power*) an area of more than a thousand square miles was contaminated following an explosion at a waste dump near Chelyabinsk. Unconfirmed reports put the death toll at 'several hundred, perhaps thousands' and the affected area is reported still to be under restriction.

Interestingly, British Atomic Energy officials like Sir John Hill were eager to discount Medvedev's reports of this accident as 'science fiction'. It seems that when it comes to nuclear safety Western and Soviet technocrats speak with one voice.

## The Role of the Left in the West

Some marxist groups have decided to ignore or play down the issue, believing that their energies are better spent on conventional organising issues nearer to the problems faced by working people: environmental and amenity issues and community politics generally are often seen as too diffuse.

But, as we have sought to indicate in earlier chapters, nuclear power raises a number of issues of direct relevance to working people and in particular the labour movement. It represents an attempt by capitalism to cope with some of its internal contradictions by introducing a 'technical fix' designed to maintain the status quo.

Technological issues have gradually emerged as bargaining issues within industry over the past decade—for example in the areas of health and safety, job design and product diversification. The recession has forced several groups of workers to begin to challenge the type of production they are engaged in.

The question of 'energy policy' is no longer an abstract one for many workers in the energy-supply and power-engineering industries. Workers at Parsons, GEC, Clarke-Chapman and Babcock & Wilcox have begun to question whether continued investment in capital-intensive large-scale power plants will guarantee long-term job security—although given the sharpness of the struggle for control fought out between the unions, the government and Arnold Weinstock, it's not surprising that, for the moment the unions continue to think in terms of large units like Drax B.

As we have seen most of the trade unions and the TUC have been unfailing in their support for nuclear power so far, in the belief that it will guarantee jobs and prosperity. One task for the left is to demonstrate that this is not so.

The Lucas Aerospace Combine Shop Stewards Committee have already come out against nuclear power, although, in common with most of the other anti-nuclear groups in the labour movement, their main fears are related to safety, environmental impact, proliferation and terrorism, rather than specifically trade union or industrial concerns. It is clearly vital that the left within the labour movement develops a *political* and *economic* critique of nuclear power, that transcends the narrower environmental criticisms.

This is not to suggest that the main aim of the left's involvement on this issue within the labour movement should be to mobilise the unions against nuclear power, as a goal in itself. The point is rather that this issue will enable workers to develop a much more radical critique, backed up by industrial strength, of the working of the capitalist system. The aim is thus 'consciousness-raising' on a broad front, rather than single-issue politics.

What does this mean in practice? It means providing technical and economic arguments for shop stewards in the energy sector and elsewhere to use as part of an attempt to expand the range of issues covered by collective bargaining. It means lobbying labour movement, trade union and labour party conferences and meetings. It also means working within the anti-nuclear movement to ensure that it is made aware of trade union and labour movement concerns.

There are a number of radical organisations seeking to operate in these ways. *SERA* (the Socialist Environment and Resources Association) has been actively involved in raising the nuclear power issue in the labour movement, while *BSSRS* (the British Society for Social Responsibility in Science) has a study group working on nuclear power and has organised a series of public meetings on the topic. The *Political Ecology Research Group* (PERG) at Oxford has been undertaking detailed studies on the social and political issues.

At the same time the various apolitical environmental groups— *Friends of the Earth* and the *Conservation Society*—have been heavily involved in researching the technical issues.

Many of these groups have local branches and there are a number of (often more militant) local anti-nuclear organisations such as *Half-Life* in Cumbria and *Scram* in Scotland. *The Nuclear Information Network* performs a co-ordinating role for many of these groups.

Obviously these various groups differ in their degree of political sophistication and in the extent of their involvement with the labour movement. But the potential is there, both for the radicalisation of otherwise apolitical environmentalists and the forging of links between the anti-nuclear and labour movements.

It is important that the wider anti-nuclear movement should develop, and the work of local and national environmental groups and student organisations like SANE (Students Against Nuclear Energy) should be supported. At the same time, the opportunity which exists in the UK to link up with the trade unions right from the start should not be overlooked. Demonstrations and direct action campaigns are valuable, but action by organised labour is likely to have far more effect.

With this in mind, the anti-nuclear movement should concern itself with the problems faced by workers in the nuclear industry and elsewhere. Only by demonstrating awareness of their viewpoints and interests will there be any hope of winning support from trade unionists for an anti-nuclear policy.

It is therefore vital that the movement make clear that, while it is against nuclear power in general, it supports and accepts the rights of workers at present in the industry to maintain and improve their conditions of employment.

The key issues for workers in the nuclear industry would seem to be those relating to health and safety and the possibility of infringement of trade union rights. In regard to the latter it could be, as was discussed earlier, that these rights are not compatible with the security needs of the industry—in which case workers in it may have to consider their commitment as trade unionists to the further expansion of the industry. At the very least, they can be alerted to the problem and seek assurances from their employers. On the question of health and safety, the research resources of some of the environmental and radical science groups could well be used to provide trade unionists in the industry with information on health and safety problems likely to effect them. The provision of practical help of this sort might mean that their general environmental and social arguments would gain more sympathetic hearing.

In terms of the wider trade union movement, the key issues, apart from health and safety and trade union rights, would seem to be the general economic and employment implications of different technologies and their relation to industrial strategy. Some anti-nuclear groups—for example the US Clamshell Alliance—have already tried to build links with workers on the basis of the employment issue, and this has, of course, been of central concern to SERA in the UK.

A key step in this task is to develop and disseminate a convincing alternative energy strategy—demonstrating that there is a viable alternative to nuclear power that involves less risks, creates more jobs and presents fewer threats to trade unionism. It is not enough simply to criticise and oppose nuclear power: it is vital that the positive advantages of a non-nuclear strategy are spelt out.

# Nuclear power and the trade unions: some practical suggestions for trade unionists

In September 1975 the Australian Council of Trade Unions carried a resolution banning the mining, handling and export of uranium on grounds of the dangers associated with the uranium fuel cycle. In May 1976, a railway shunting supervisor was suspended after refusing to move mining material—and this precipitated a major nation-wide rail strike in support of his reinstatement.[1]

Trade-union action on this scale seems a long way off in the UK, although in November 1975 the local section of the Confederation of Shipbuilding and Engineering Unions (CSEU) tried, unsuccessfully, to put a ban on the handling of nuclear wastes coming into the docks at Barrow, en route to Windscale. The district secretary commented: 'We condemn the dumping of nuclear waste in Britain and call on the confederation to do all in its power at national level to oppose this.' Opposition came from the GMWU which has members working at Windscale, and the ban was never enforced.

Outright 'blacking' of nuclear work would seem to be too ambitious a goal at the present stage in the UK. The issues involved have to be far more widely appreciated in the trade union movement before widespread support can be expected.

Generalised 'anti-nuclear' motions at trade union conferences and the TUC Congress, like that tabled by NALGO in 1977, clearly have a role to play in opening up the debate, as have the campaigning activities of groups like Energy 2000.[2]

At the same time, problems relating to nuclear power are increasingly likely to impinge on trade unionists on a day-to-day basis. Workers in the nuclear industry itself will obviously be concerned with issues such as pay, conditions, health and safety, productivity, manning levels, training and long-term planning and so on. They—and the trade union movement in general—may also be concerned at the possibility of infringement of trade-union rights. Clearly it is bad trade-union practice to cede to management the right to decide (ostensibly on safety or security grounds) when a strike is legitimate or what technical information can and cannot be disclosed to shop stewards or trade-union-appointed safety representatives. It would seem vital for the union representatives involved to secure assurances and, if possible, negotiate agreements on these questions.

Workers not directly linked to the nuclear industry may be affected by health and safety issues—for example people employed in transporting nuclear materials by land, sea, or air. Trade unionists in other industries will also have a more general interest in nuclear power. For example, what implications does it have for overall economic policy and industrial strategy, for trade-union rights and for employment?

The 'checklist' at the end of this chapter is essentially a list of questions which trade unionists can pursue now, either within their unions or in negotiations with their employers. Some of these questions might form the basic of requests for information under the disclosure provisions of the Employment Protection Act (EPA) or Health and Safety at Work Act (HSWA).

Under the HSWA's 'Regulations on Safety Representatives and Safety Committees' which come into force in October 1978, workers' safety representatives can obtain information from employers concerning changes to plant, equipment and materials, the toxicity of any substances used, hazards, the results of any related measurements made, records of accidents, diseases and sickness, and so on. They also have a right to technical information from (other) manufacturers and suppliers and from the Health and Safety Executive. The ACAS code of practice on 'Disclosure of Information to Trade Unions for Collective Bargaining Purposes' (HMSO 1977) outlines the type of information companies should disclose under the EPA. Information on technical development plans, investment programmes manpower policies and so on would clearly be relevant. Of course there are let-out clauses: companies need not disclose information that would entail too much extra work or expenditure, or which would be of use by competitors—or, as we noted in Part 2, information that had national security implications. Long-term planning information might also be available via the Planning Agreement System, and the disclosure provisions of the Industries Act are relevant here. Planning agreements between the government and companies are meant to cover investment, productivity, employment and product development programmes, and are supposed to be subject to trade-union consultation and approval.

In presenting suggestions for questions and demands we are not trying to pre-empt the activities and judgement of trade-union representatives in the nuclear industry or anywhere else. We seek only to stimulate consideration of issues which might otherwise be foregone. Discussion and debate is the lifeblood of trade-union democracy. It may be that, for example, trade union representatives will be able to obtain suitable assurances—and, hopefully, formal negotiated *agreements*—on the freedom of disclosure of information. At the Windscale Enquiry, the chairman of the trade union side of the BNFL Joint Industrial Council stated that '. . . we have every confidence that the limitation of information will be confined to the very narrow limits that are genuinely needed for security reasons'. (Transcript 82, 14 June 1977)

Such assurances are obviously welcome—but they should not prevent discussion and debate on the underlying problems and their implications.

## Some Key Questions for Trade Unionists

1. What radio-active materials are in use in your firm or establishment? (eg many workers may be unaware of the widespread use of isotopes in industry) What safety precautions are in existence? Are they adequate?

2. Does the Official Secrets Act or any other provision for national security cover any work done at your firm or establishment? Does this inhibit the operation of the Health and Safety at Work Act, the Employment Protection Act or trade union rights generally?

3. To what extent is your company involved in nuclear power work? How significant is its investment in this field? Are there plans for further involvement—and if so what are the employment implications?

4. To what extent could your firm contribute to the development of alternative energy technologies? Could a product diversification campaign by shop stewards be a way to ensure long term job security?

Trade union research departments may be able to provide advice on some of the health and safety, technical and economic issues, and as mentioned earlier, there are a number of voluntary organisations who can provide relevant advice, such as the BSSRS Hazards Group and SERA (both at 9 Poland Street, London W1).

The Centre for Alternative Industrial and Technological Systems at North East London Polytechnic (Longbridge Road, Dagenham, Essex) set up by the Lucas Aerospace Combine Shop Stewards Committee in conjunction with NELP, may also be able to offer advice on product diversification options.

For a brief guide to some of the health and safety issues see chapter 5 above.

## References

1 See *Chain Reaction*, Vol. 2 No. 2 for a full report. The ban on existing mining operations has since been lifted following the Australian unions' acceptance of the findings of the Ranger report but it remains valid with regard to new mines and the nuclear issue is still a key one in union circles.

2 It is also worth nothing that in response to the Irish government's plan for a reactor at Carnsore Point, the Irish Transport and General Workers' Union has expressed 'grave reservation' about the wisdom of going nuclear. The French union CFDT also is highly critical of the nuclear industry—particularly in regard to health and safety conditions at the Cap la Hague reprocessing works.

**Further reading**

*Nuclear Power* by Walt Patterson of Friends of the Earth is a good general introduction to the technical and historical facts but contains few political insights (80p. Penguin 1976). Walt Patterson's *The Fissile Society* (Earth Resources Research 1977) focuses more specially on the UK institutional context.
*The Hazards of Nuclear Power* by Alan Roberts and Zhores Medvedev is an excellent socialist analysis of the politics of nuclear power (95p. Spokesman 1977).

Royal Commission on Environmental Pollution *Sixth Report* Cmnd. 6618 (1976) £2.65. The Flowers Report—by far the most comprehensive and unbiased 'official' account of nuclear technology and its implications.

There are several accounts of the Windscale Enquiry and of the issues that were discussed at it (I don't include the Parker report amongst these) although, as yet, none which locates it within a broad political context. But see Czech Conroy's *What Choice Windscale* (£1 PDC 1978) for a good survey of the issues, and Ian Breach's *The Windscale Enquiry* (£1 IPC 1978). Breach's *Windscale Fallout* (90p. Penguin Special 1978) is also worth looking at.

One of the best assessments of UK energy options currently available comes from NALGO—*Energy: A Planned Policy*, a report by NALGO's Energy Policy Advisory Committee January 1978. (Available from 1 Mabledon Place, London WC1.) Although not explicitly anti-nuclear, this report argues for immediate investment in renewable alternatives, particularly solar.

Amory Lovins *Soft Energy Paths* (95p. Penguin 1977) provides a useful overview of the alternative energy options, although it lacks a solid political perspective.

*Undercurrents* Magazine (27 Clerkenwell Road, London EC1) regularly provides a good critical analysis of nuclear politics and news of alternative technology developments.

Pluto Press's *Big Red Diary* for 1979 is on the politics of nuclear power.

**UK Organisations**

Socialist Environment and Resources Association (SERA)
British Society for Social Responsibility in Science (BSSRS)
Friends of the Earth
all 9 Poland Street, London W1

Nuclear Information Network
29 St James Street, London WC1N 3ES

Political Ecology Research Group
P.O. Box 14, Oxford.

Scottish Campaign to Resist the Atomic Menace (SCRAM)
2a Ainslie Place, Edinburgh 3

Energy 2000
64 Salisbury Road, Sheffield S10 1WB

# Big Red Diary 1979

Better Active Today than Radioactive Tomorrow

Research and text Dave Smith with help from the *Undercurrents* collective.

The accident that could happen only twice in a million million years occurred in a nuclear reactor outside Chicago on 5 June 1970.

Each year Pluto Press produces a Big Red (pocket) Diary, or Calendar, on a matter of current interest. This year the topic is nuclear power—what it is, who wants it and why, what are its implications for jobs, health, social and political arrangements, and who is campaigning against it—from the Clamshell Alliance in the US to the Burger Initiatives in Germany.

The diary presents these issues in anecdote and analysis, in pictures and text, in three colours and in a form as attractive as it is useful.